Puto

Veracruz Pedroza Sánchez

Printed in the United States of America First Printing: February 2018

Paperback ISBN: 978-1-62747-246-3
ebook ISBN: 978-1-62747-247-0

Books by Veracruz Pedroza Sánchez
Prison Letters: Walking to Honor
Puto

Articles published in the San Diego Free Press:
From Hockey Star to Homeless: Craig Miller Dies on Christmas Day in Ocean Beach
Son of Ocean Beach Homeless Man Qualifies for the Olympics

Articles published in Casino City Times:
Great Players Need Great Coaches
Craps Characters I've Met
Win the MVP of Craps Play
Being the Batting Champ
Mexican Food and the Martingale
The Mean Priest and Dice Control Teams
Baseball Teaches Teamwork at Casino Gambling
Bookstores, Books, and Truth
Advantage Players Need to Train like Money Mayweather
Ladies and Gentleman, Here They Are: The Beatles

For the women of mother earth
Para las mujeres de la madre tierra

In Memoriam of
Martha Pedroza

"The feeling of love and it won't be missing for it was always there,
and it will always be there."

CONTENTS

FOREWARD ix

PREFACE xi

CHAPTER ONE: PUTO 1

CHAPTER TWO: NO DICK, SMALL DICK 3

CHAPTER THREE: MEXICAN OR NAH 7

CHAPTER FOUR: ARSON 11

CHAPTER FIVE: PRIMA FRANCES 17

CHAPTER SIX: DEANNA 21

CHAPTER SEVEN: DIVORCED PARENTS 25

CHAPTER EIGHT: UNJUSTIFIED REACTION 29

CHAPTER NINE: FIRST KISS 33

CHAPTER TEN: BIG PUTO, LIL' PUTO 35

CHAPTER ELEVEN: LA MARCHA 39

CHAPTER TWELVE: SIBLING LOVE 43

CHAPTER THIRTEEN: CHOLULA 49

CHAPTER FOURTEEN: LARRY 57

CHAPTER FIFTEEN: EASTER 61

CHAPTER SIXTEEN: A BEATING OR TWO 63

CHAPTER SEVENTEEN: FUNCTIONING DRUNK..................... 67

CHAPTER EIGHTEEN: MISCARRIAGE....................................... 69

CHAPTER NINETEEN: BROWN BAG 73

CHAPTER TWENTY: NANCY 77

CHAPTER TWENTY-ONE: JUNIOR.. 81

CHAPTER TWENTY-TWO: SANDRITA.. 83

CHAPTER TWENTY-THREE: ROOM 443 85

CHAPTER TWENTY-FOUR: UNOPENED PRISON LETTER...... 99

CHAPTER TWENTY-FIVE: NOVEMBER 23RD 103

CHAPTER TWENTY-SIX: CHOLA.. 105

CHAPTER TWENTY-SEVEN: BEAUTIFUL THERAPY 107

CHAPTER TWENTY-EIGHT: UNDOCUMENTED
VALEDICTORIAN... 111

CHAPTER TWENTY-NINE: MI BARRIO THROUGH
THE YEARS.. 115

CHAPTER THIRTY: MINERVA... 119

CHAPTER THIRTY-ONE: 10:00 P.M. CALL................................ 123

CHAPTER THIRTY-TWO: CALL TO THE VIRG....................... 125

CHAPTER THIRTY-THREE: FINAL GOODBYE 127

CHAPTER THIRTY-FOUR: PHILIPPIANS 4:13 135

CHAPTER THIRTY-FIVE: FIN.. 137

EPILOGUE: NAH, NOT QUITE FINISH YET 143

ACKNOWLEDGMENTS 145

FOREWARD

Don't think you can keep breaking your woman's heart
Thin Line Between Love and Hate, The Persuaders, 1971

What does it take for a woman to call a man a Puto?

What did he do to her, to make her lose all respect for him?

What amount of damage could he have done to a woman to make her call him out in a public shaming, that is more often used to devalue women?

Men underestimate the power of women. Women underestimate their own power.

Puto is a testament to that, for it revolves around a woman's heartbreak: Vera's heartbreak. An entire accumulation of her life's heartbreaks, and those are many for a woman in the peak of her mid-30s.

Hence, *Puto* is also a sequel to Sanchez' first book, *Prison Letters*, though both can be read alone or in sequence. With this second publication, Sanchez' body of work solidifies her raw voice and lightening presence in Chicano/a literature, especially writing from and about one of the most iconic Chicano places: Barrio Logan.

For instance, *Easter,* is a candid and innocent moment of brown children being sun-kissed in their porch steps, caressing life and being touched by the surrounding natural forces of the ghetto.

Her sense of belonging and growing up in Logan as well as her kinship to the Chicano band Los Alacranes (her uncles are Ramon "Chunky" and Rick Sanchez, the brothers of her father, Ralph) are indelible and fill the pages with personal childhood memories and stories heard unfiltered, straight and dirty from her legendary uncles, especially if they were drunk.

The tenderness and the unveiling of family drama in *Room 443* as "Chunky laid in the hospital bed compressed in a blanket" humanizes and reminds us all that even the icons are ravaged by personal pains, afflictions, and regrets.

Puto, though, is entirely about a woman's complications with her life, and the unending heartbreaks endured: her heart first broken by her parents, by her mom and dad failing to nurture and to be there for her, as guides. Thus, she refers to them by their first names, Ralph and Maria.

Then, her body battered by the love of her life, the man that committed the ultimate beating: the rejection of their unborn baby. A loss of life inside of her, *Miscarriage*, is both the metaphor and the once living flesh that evacuated her womanhood, the little girl she so desired, that one most women desire to hold in their caring arms.

A woman's heart, though, is made of flesh, not bone. She did not have broken pieces to put back together. She had an organ to mend, to soothe back into constellation of veins of living splendor.

A woman's body is the strongest entity in the world, it can be bruised, it can be cut, but it can prevail assaults, and it gives and sheds light, and life.

Puto is ultimately about a woman's journey through an uneasy life. Reading it reminded me of Etta James' moaning in pain and struggle within the conflicted insides of a woman's soul.

Reading it was listening to Vera's insides, to her own recording of Etta's *Feeling Uneasy* but ultimately letting the intimate terror go away, making way for a new beginning on earth.

Vera's earthly right to moan in pleasure, again, and with a mended heart.

Rosiangela Escamilla
La Mesa, California
January 2018

PREFACE

A message to my reader: I will invite you on my life journey, with you in the VIP section as my special guest. The events you will soon read are true, harsh at times, funny at times, but nonetheless, honest. My initial intentions, at first, were to write for me, but during the writing process, I realized it was for you, to help you heal.

With great pain, blossoms a beautiful story in you that must be written. Everyone has experienced pain, whether through a partner, spouse, parents, family member, friends, or a child. We had to come to terms with ourselves and begin the healing process of moving forward. Forgiveness, no matter who we hurt or who has hurt us, is needed to move forward, so we can give back love. With my pain, emerged my best writing (so far). That's the case in all artist. Frida Kahlo illustrated some of the best works of art that embraced the world through her miscarriages and cheating husband. Music artists like Eminem, Pink, and Adele needed to confront their addictions and heartbreaks to release their creative lyrics. We can choose the path of self-destruction or we can take our pain to unleash the creative force inside us. The world needs your story now more than ever. Allow yourself to grow, heal, forgive, and love. Some of you have gone through the same pain and some are currently going through it.

I would be lying to you if I said writing my book was easy. Many times, I had to stop writing because I was reminiscing about the pain, but the thought of helping my reader kept me pushing to the final pages. For that, I owe you a great deal of gratitude. Sharing the stories of my ten year relationship, my family stories, and observations from women who I admire, shaped me into a stronger person by the end of my book. I wrote these stories and poems in my journal, tucked away for years, keeping them to myself, until now. Points of views will shift; narrators will take turns; I will play my role as the main character; sometimes, I will be a distant narrator, but I am there every step of the way with my reader.

My weakness left me the day I decided to kill the old me, but not without learning some valuable lessons along the way. Once I made that decision, there was no looking back. By the end of the book, I promise you will be in a better place with yourself. To anyone who has experienced a broken heart, it will heal. This is our incredible journey together, our stories, our pain, and our healing. To my reader, I present to you, *Puto*.

CHAPTER ONE

PUTO

You have a side bitch named Monica, the one with those goofy bug eyes and frizzy mop, the cock teasing girl you wanted since junior high. The one you made out with at the playground, and your girlfriend at the time caught you in action, but all you did was kiss Mop Head harder. Instead of lip-locking with Mop Head, make her useful, flip that bitch upside down, and clean the floor with her.

Monica, the dumbass Pisces and, you, the manipulative Libra. Mother was right about you, so were my *tias* and sisters and *primas* and girlfriends. A woman's intuition is never wrong. So what the fuck was I thinking?

You spent your shifts sneaking away during lunch, an easy getaway since she only lived down the street from the catholic school where you spent your days as a minimum wage security guard and evenings as a washed up wrestling coach because you can't get over the fact that you never made it to the state championships. Wrestling moves that you grappled with Monica in the sack when you accidentally butt dialed my number.

"Oh yes, baby."

"Cum inside me. Fuck me harder."

You moaned together, and you pulled out your toddler pee-pee, the sweat running down your hairy ass back. The pussy was magic. She knew exactly how to wheel you in waiting to be her next meal. You kissed her on the cheek, and she laughed, pushed you away, wanting more, and you went for it. Little Miss Ha Ha Ha, "Stop it. Come back when your girlfriend is not around." You couldn't help but think of humping her leg, while you jacked off watching porn.

You bragged to your cronies, your chest grew bigger, but your soul, non-existent. And when I was lying on the couch when I lost our little one, you said, "I have to go to work."

She knows you belonged to another, no strings attached for an easy fuck. She's your true sweetheart, the pussy that smells and tastes like rotten fish, protein at its finest. Still, she never committed to you, and it drove you fucking crazy because, in the end, no one wants a short, fat, bald, half-Mexican, half-Puerto Rican broke ass nigga, like you.

You never denied your *cochino* acts, like the asshole your bitch ass mother raised you to be or was it your punk ass father, the one who also seeks the average *nalgas* in town, the one that advised you to always keep three bitches on the side at the bare minimum.

But in the midst of deleting text messages, changing passwords, pretending to come home from work, the stories you pondered in your head, begging your boys to cover for you, airing out the perfume from your shirt, scrambling to make your portion of rent because you had a wild night out, defaulting on your student loans, somewhere in that fucked up brain of yours, you forgot that the *other* girl, your girlfriend of ten years, was a writer. And before you shut the door for the last time, you said, "Maybe one day you'll write about it." So I will, so I did, and now you, Puto, will be famous. Here is your story, and this is how it started.

CHAPTER TWO

NO DICK,
SMALL DICK

Your pencil dick is so small, when you insert it into a pussy, any pussy, there's a gap. With all the women you dated, have fucked, we all say the same thing, "Puto might as well have no dick, like the Ken doll."

With legs spread, hips up, from behind, a backwards ride, sit me on top of the kitchen counter, or the edge of the bed, still *nada*, nothing, zero. I wish I could fake it, but I was bored. That sperm count was low. Don't even bother taking viagra; there's no point of getting a little dick hard unless one needs a good laugh. Even Frida Kahlo couldn't be that creative with your shit. You only need two fingers to stroke it, but that small dick of your has gotten you into loads of trouble. Like the time you went to a frat party picking up on chicks. One chick's man watched you, got pissed, and smashed a hammer against your face, leaving that scar above your lip. After that, you still didn't learn your lesson.

Ali was one victim of your sorry ass pick up lines. You and your boys cruised to Triple Crown. Made up another story how you and I broke up that weekend, so nobody would call you on your shit when you pursued Ali, slipped her your number and agreed to a dinner night that led to many. She also went to the Bay, so you could jump right into the conversations of catching up after high school. Again, *baboso*, dumbass, you forgot that I also attended the same school, so information was even easier to obtain in that small circle of gossip. How lovely to wine and dine her for the four months you dated each other. "I never had to pull out my wallet," Ali willing disclosed everything after we both realized we were getting played.

Ali finished a game at a nearby soccer field. Her teammates agreed to grab a few beers at Triple Crown after their victory. You recognized Ali from the Bay since she had the same bleached hair and pale freckled face. At the time, it was no sweat for you to sneak around because you were living in your boy's garage. "It makes sense why he never invited me over to his house. He didn't have one." You flipped through the San Diego Reader, planning for local concerts and eateries. You covered all expenses, while I paid your bills because that old ass "I have student loans" bullshit was your go-to card.

On Thanksgiving, the day where you're supposed to give thanks for the family and friends in your life, we went to your dad's house, but I was sick with a cold, heading home early. You kissed me on the forehead and said, "Have a good night and get some rest, sweetheart." You deceived me, pretending to stay with your dad, who always covered for you. Instead, you dialed Ali, who was getting off work, driving the 45 minutes to her house, spending the holidays together. When you arrived, you undressed her and sucked on her A cup titties. You unbuckled your pants and pulled out a condom. "If we do this, then it's official." That freaked you the fuck out. "I was cheating on by my ex-fiancee, so I always have my guard up for guys like him. I called him a few times after that, but he didn't pick up the phone. Never heard from him after that."

It was that same Trojan you pulled out when paying for your portion of breakfast. The waitress placed the bill on the table, and you grabbed the wad of cash in your pocket, along with the infamous Magnum. I stared at the condom in disbelief, picked up my belongings, and sat in my truck. As I remained there, you brainstormed a pretty clever story, I must admit. Only a real psycho would come up with some crazy shit on the spot. Most dudes would fold, "Damn, I have to come clean." But not you.

"You know I live with Bruce. He keeps money in his dresser. I had to borrow money from him, and I must've taken the condom my accident. Look me in the eyes," I turned away even more. "Please. Look me in the eyes. I would never cheat on you, sweetheart. Trust me." You said it with such compassion, a sympathetic tone in your words.

I started my truck and replied, "Okay."

CHAPTER THREE

MEXICAN OR NAH

Adolf Hitler would be fucking proud of you. You blamed your lies on your mom. It was her fault she changed your last name. Your mom, the short *negra*, who looked like a deformed Chaka Khan, wanted all her sons' names to match so she wouldn't have to explain why she had more than one baby daddy, a very convincing story. I see where you inherited your storytelling skills. This is the bullshit you fed me for years, and like a dumbass, I believed you. I believed one day you would change your name back to your Mexican grassroots, as you promised, but nah. I was fucking wrong, again.

So the real story goes your colonized ass convinced Chaka Khan to revise your last name, sending her to the courthouse, standing in those long ass lines, and paying for the legal fees. You would be able to pass for an Indian, Italian, Haitian, even an Eskimo. Anything but a fucking Beaner.

You saved your paycheck to buy blonde dye and board shorts. When your counselor asked what foreign language class you wanted to take to graduate high school, you answered, "German." You confessed to your boys, "Yeah bro, like I'd bang Selma Hayek even though she's a brunette." You surfed, skated, grew out your nappy hair, and lived by the beach.

Neither of your parents wanted to watch your problematic ass during the summer, so they shipped you off to Abuelita, but only in Abuelita's house, she expected a response in her native tongue. When you called her grandma, she corrected you, "En Español." You surrendered because no one was around to tease you. She made you *café* in the mornings with *chorizo con huevos*. You sat at her table, chewed with your mouth closed, and you weren't dismissed until you ate all your food. You spoke kind words like, "*con permiso,*" and "*por favor.*" You washed the dishes, took out the trash, and watered the plants in Abuelita's garden. When you spent the night, she patted your head as you fell asleep in her palms, and she woke you up in the morning with a kiss on the forehead.

Abuelita, warm skin and unerring eyes, was from Jalisco. At ten years old, she slipped across *la frontera*, the border, to pick tomatoes with her father and brothers, a daughter in a family that only praised their sons. By twelve, Abuelita was the woman of the *campo*, packing crates of grapes, plums, strawberries, and oranges faster than any of the *campesinos*. As she developed into a young lady, she sang mariachi songs at bars for loose change, the *pistiadores,* the drunks sliding drinks her way insisting they were single, but Abuelita, with her third eye of wisdom, knew better. She was nicknamed La Chula, the first to wear high heels and red lipstick to school. Her black hair pinned back, and her skirt hugged the curves in her hips. The schoolboys lined up to carry her journal savoring the smell of her perfume, kissing her hand along the way. La Chula didn't waste her time with them, rather spent the evenings in the library reading poems by Pablo Neruda and studying for her next exam. And although every boy tried every day, they knew they couldn't have her.

Abuelita's house smelled like the sun sprinkled with holy water. Her table covered in a *zarape* with a bottle of tequila at the center to remind her of *la hacienda*, the ranch. She prayed in her rocking chair for God to protect you as she squinted through the curtains watching over you. She called you "*mijo,*" laughed at your jokes, cooked you homemade *tortillas*, cleaned your wounds, and hugged you when you walked through the door. After you were done playing, she prepared *saladitos* and sliced cucumbers topped with *Tajín* as a snack. The radio

8

played music from Lola Beltrán, and together, you danced in the living room to *Paloma Negra*, Abuelta's tiny feet tapping with the earth as she spun you in a circle. She dressed you in a *charro* suit, snapped a picture, and hung it on her wall because she was proud of you. And even for Abuelita, you smiled.

On your birthday, Abuelita placed a silver box in your lap. You untied the ribbon without hesitation. Abuelita knitted a blanket the color of soft sand. "It will keep you safe, my dear. Wrap it around you whenever you are scared, and I will be there," Abuelita said in Spanish. Those were her last words to you.

When Abuelita passed away, you went back to your *pendejada* ways. "Do it yourself!" You argued with your mom, throwing the dish towel in her face. You ignored the signs in your neighborhood that read no skating allowed, crossed it out with a black sharpie, and hocked a loogie on the sidewalk as you scratched your balls. You blasted your death metal music loud enough for the world to hear even after the cops cited your mom with a ticket for disturbing the peace. You grabbed girls in their asses when they crossed your path, high-fiving your boys because you were so cool. When Mr. Budnick returned your exam with a much deserved F, you tore it up and screamed if you didn't graduate, you would kick the shit out of him. The child that Abuelita once embraced with a smile, the child she wrapped in her arms, the child she kept safe, was now gone. Your knitted blanket collected dust, hidden in a silver box in a garage, forgotten like your inner child, and you never spoke another Spanish word again.

CHAPTER FOUR

ARSON

I was known as the crazy bitch around town after that night. Friends I hadn't heard from in years hit me up asking if it was true. As word of mouth spread quickly, I became the latest *chisme* at local bars in Pacific Beach, something for his boys to gossip about as they chugged their beers leading into the early morning stumbling back to his studio apartment.

The first time we met I originally thought he would be a one night stand as intended. In my journal, I scribbled the names of every guy who rejected me, crossing out each name, because I "wasn't what they were looking for" or "it's me, not you," bullshit. The list grew to a couple of pages front and back, so when I came across his social media page, we began chatting, exchanging phone numbers. When he called, I immediately blushed when he said his name. Agreeing to meet up at the Blue Foot Bar by the end of the week, he promised, "I have all the kisses in the world for those pretty luscious lips of yours."

By the time he showed up at Blue Foot, I was already a few tequila shots in, feeling loose and warm. I posted in the back of the bar, crossing my legs, checking my hair and make-up before he walked in. We made eye contact from across the bar as he nodded with confidence strutting in my direction. As he reached for me, he grabbed a chunk of my long black hair, putting it back and stuck his tongue down my throat. The ladies next to us were even engaged in our kiss, "Damn," they shouted, but we didn't stop.

We ordered more shots, and the rest of the night was a blur. If we spoke, I didn't remember. If I fell, I didn't remember. If we fucked, I didn't remember, and that is how the night ended. I woke up naked in my bed with him lying next to me. The room smelled like ass. I touched my lower lips, slimy with his cum, my bed covered in wet spots.

"I drove you home," he said as he opened his eyes.

"How did you know where I lived?"

"Your driver's license." He popped out of my bed and found his jeans tangled with my underwear. He fastened his pants throwing his shirt over his shoulders, "I have to run to wrestling practice. I'll call you later," and he was out the door. Nobody ever called me back after they tapped my ass, but to my surprise, a few days later, he did. I ripped out the pages in my journal of the guys who rejected me because I had finally found someone.

But, again, I was a stupid bitch. The first clue was when we met up for the second time, this time with his boys. He didn't even greet me with a kiss, just a random hi. He ordered a round of beers for the table.

"Damn girl, you look good," he groaned rubbing the waitress on her back. He sized her up and down, another cute skinny blonde. I silently stood across the table, but he didn't notice me eyeballing him or he didn't seem to care, but I stuck around. Maybe it was a mistake for me to be there, while I listened to him share wrestling stories of how he beat the shit out of this guy and how he fucked the shit out of this girl. He's with his boys, I persuaded myself, giving an excuse as to why I felt so small. After the bar, we cruised back to his studio to fuck, and I gave it up every time. It was an easy way for him to keep seeing me, a guaranteed piece of ass.

I knew the news would eventually come since a burning sensation stung as I pissed, "You just have to get over it or else we're not going to work out."

"Who is she?"

"A girl in the complex, but that doesn't fucking matter. I told her I wanted to be with you. You should be happy about that."

"How did you find out?"

"She called me. She got tested, and it came back positive. It's not a big deal," he said as he tossed the number to Planned Parenthood, "there's one down the street. I already went in for my appointment. They gave me this powder stuff to cure it. It takes about two weeks to completely go away." He sang a Sublime song as he stood up from the couch to grab a beer from the fridge. He cracked it open and chugged. "You didn't want kids, anyways." And I just agreed with him.

On his 30th birthday, it was another drunken marathon as usual, the alcohol poured itself as everyone crammed into his studio. The Chargers secured a victory, and the celebration grew intense. Mixed shots of cheap bottles passed around in a circle. I took my fair share, eventually passing out on the couch. The room was spinning, and I buried my head in a pillow covered with my drool. It was hard to breathe until my eyes finally shut. I don't know how long I stayed passed out, but when I woke up, it was dark, and I was alone.

I always heard of crazy bitches who destroyed their man's belongings, cutting holes in his clothes or slashing his tires. I had never done anything like that until now. By this time, his flirting, his STD, his trips to the strip club, my loneliness, built inside me, and I let it out in the most violent way, picking up random shit that were in my reach and throwing it like a baseball across the room: bottles, lamps, ashtrays, dishes, even a painting I gifted for him when his childhood friend hung himself because his girlfriend left him for another dude. As junk piled into the kitchen area, a cloth lying on top of the stove caught on fire. I stumbled to the sink to fill a glass with water, putting out the fire with the glass. Since there were no windows in his studio, I slid the back door open to air out the place.

"What the fuck are you doing, you psycho bitch!" his brother screamed shoving me out of the way. Later in the court documents, I found out that his brother returned to the studio for the pills he forgot before heading to the tittie bar for more partying with the birthday boy. More names launched my way, so I left, leaving them with the mess. A crazy Mexican bitch with scraggly black hair and sleeve tattoos was easy to spot in the beach community. That's how the cops were able to identify me when they found me as I walked down the street catching me off guard. "You are under arrest for arson." The cop folded my hands behind my back and tightly handcuffed my wrist pressing my face on the hood of the cop car. I was groped for weapons and narcotics, and the cop pushed me into the back seat.

I was driven to Las Colinas, the women's prison, where my mugshot was taken, and I was booked on felony charges. The holding cell smelled like shit, benches covered in filth, and the ventilation turned up to its max. Some ladies were passed out on the floor, others stood. I posted on the corner of the bench and hugged myself since I wasn't wearing a jacket at the time of my arrest.

"You cold, honey? They be up in here wanting us to freeze to death," a hefty lady wrapped her arms around me, "my name is Opal, darling." Opal looked like she was in here a time or two. Gashes stretched across the top of her eye. She squeezed me tighter, "No need to be scared, first timer. We have each other's back up in here." Opal was arrested for beating up her boyfriend, again. "I dragged him to the ground and beat his ass. I done told this heffer I'd put hands on him if he touched me like that. Fool found out the hard way I ain't playing with his ass."

As a little girl, Opal was molested by her grandfather, and she promised herself that, at no cost, will a man ever touch her like that again. Her father was shot by the police, which plunged her mother into prostitution, leaving Opal to be raised by the streets. When she found an eviction notice taped to the front door, she had no choice but to drop out of high school to slang rocks, a trade dominated by the men on the block. Opal wouldn't even flinch at gunpoint. Just gave the gunman the money and the drugs then went about her average day. Although school wasn't much of a priority, Opal missed the free food, school being the only time she ate. "I had to feed myself, dress myself, and protect myself." Opal was an exception to the rules of the hustle game. Her knuckles were hard, and her chin was even harder. She could take a stiff one to the jaw if a dude was close enough to connect. When she wasn't running in the streets, she was found in the boxing gym sparring with grown men. "I had to. It was survive or die for me. I was walking down an alley where I usually found leftover meals thrown in the dumpster. When I was digging through one of them trash cans, I came across this here flyer that advertised for a month worth of free boxing lessons. I didn't have anything to lose. Might as well give it a shot. They done laugh at me when I first walked in, but I had so much anger built inside of me, I let it all out in that ring. I always caught them with my left hook. Them heffers never seen it coming," she slapped her knee with passion, "Coach Padilla saw potential in me and took me under his wings. He was, and still to this day, my only father figure."

Coach Padilla trained Opal under the condition that she completed her G.E.D. At her graduation ceremony, he surprised her with a boxing charm and platinum chain. When she opened the box, she cried, for the first time, tears of joy. She never owned anything of value or at least anything she didn't hawk from suburban homes.

As an amateur boxer, Opal was undefeated, ready to turn pro, but she found herself back behind bars before her first professional bout, the streets always catching up to her. "I was the heavy favorite going into my first professional fight. I already earned my nickname 'The High Jacker' from the boys on my block, so the named carried over to the ring. I was in the locker room wrapping my hands, getting ready for a sparring session. Coach Padilla walked in and broke the news that he could no longer train me. At first, I thought he be playing, but then I saw the worry on his face. Coach Padilla don't be worrying like that. Three months later, he died of brain cancer, and I just couldn't take it anymore. I braided my hair in cornrows, strapped on my Dickies and wife beater, and returned to the block. Oh Lord, I really did want to be a good person," she said as she made a sign of the cross in the air. "Society gets it twisted about us locked up. We not all bad peeps."

After Opal was done telling her story, I shared the reason for my arrest. The night passed, and I pressed my head against Opal's shoulders and curled into her arms for protection. I closed my eyes, and she crest my hair, "Everything will be alright, baby girl. He won't hurt you again," her voice grew smooth, "I promise."

CHAPTER FIVE

PRIMA FRANCES

As my relationship with him prolonged over the years, I observed strong females figures to help me cope with my depression. Opal's fearless "I don't take shit from anyone" attitude sparked a small fire inside to begin the process of building my self-confidence. When I was told the story of my Prima Frances, I knew I had to eventually make a decision about my situation.

A picture of Frances hung from her sister's wall. Prima Imelda poured a bowl of menudo, a secret recipe passed down from her mother. She always brought out the red carpet for me when I paid her a visit in New Mexico for a quick weekend getaway. Using a warm *tortilla* as a spoon, I scooped a few slices of meat, the soup dripping out at the end. My eyes continued to focus on the picture; it was unique looking, black and white, Frances wearing a *sombrero* riding a tractor with her legs spread opened.

"We were a crazy bunch, *primita*. My sisters and I acted as we pleased. Too many women in one household dad complained. He put us to work inside and outside the house. We had to hold our own if we wanted a roof over our head. Never disobey a man he advised. A woman needs to learn her place, but dad was outnumbered. Twelve daughters to control, shit. Dad screamed he had the curse of the devil."

Prima Imelda began smoking at ten, drinking at eleven, "I had to hide it from my mom. If she found out, you would shove a *chancla* up my ass." That seemed to be a common discipline tactic in all Mexican families. Mexican mothers can take the most harmless object on the face of the planet, like a slipper, and turn it into a lethal weapon of mass destruction. "My sister showed me how to apply makeup, so I wouldn't act so much like a guy. She tried her best to keep me in line, but I'm a handful." Prima Imelda flipped over another *tortilla* on the *comal*, swigging her beer at the same time. "Do you want a Dos Equis?" Without answering, she cracked the bottle open using the edge of the table. "I have weed growing in the back if you want that too, a little something if you need help getting through the day. Las Cruces heat is a bitch. *Toma,* here," as she handed me the beer. Prima Imelda's fingers were tough at the tips with deep callouses on her palms. "I got use to the thorns from the vines, but I was tired of looking at my ugly hands. I wanted a husband, too, you know. That's why I became a beautician. The things girls will do for a man. You have a man, *primita*? He treats you well?"

I lied.

"As long as you're happy, and he treats you like a queen. My husband and I live in separate houses. That way we don't fight."

I drank my beer in order to avoid answering any more questions.

"My sister started seeing this guy named Sangre. He was given that name because he could make anyone bleed. Frances started to lie to my parents telling them that we attended morning mass when we were really at the park meeting Sangre. My sister had to reapply her make up before she walked through the door. I promised her it was mums the word."

The more Frances was involved with Sangre, the more lies she had to come up with, but those lies, catch up to all of us at one time or another. She could only invent so many stories before their mom suspected something and started following her daughters. "When mom caught my sister with Sangre, mom grabbed both of us by the *greñas,* whooped our asses at the same time, and dragged us all the way home by our nappy hair for another ass beating. I still remember those *chingasos*. Hurts to this day." That didn't stop Frances from sneaking out. She saw Sangre more now that the cat was out of the bag. It got to a point where she ran away from home her sophomore year, a straight A student up until she left. Months passed, and the family didn't hear for her until she showed up with her bags and a black eye. "I ran to the kitchen to grab a bag of ice. She slept in for a few days and was saying stupid shit about how she loved him, how he didn't mean it. I wasn't the one to give advice because I was caught up in my own shit. My sister went back like we all do. The beatings got worse, and her body grew weaker. It really hurt my mom. It hurt me to see her cry."

Sangre impregnated another church girl turned sinner. Frances tried to go back even after she heard the news, but he greeted her with a fist to her chest, her chest turned the color of bark. A woman can only take so many beatings until she has to make two choices: leave or die.

Frances gave the doctors a bunch of excuses, how it was the pesticides from working in the field or how the labor equipment fell on her or how the bosses made her work overtime, fifteen hour shifts, in that dry heat. "We gathered around her bed, and I placed her makeup bag by her side. Mom lit a candle dimming the lights to say our prayers." The sisters held each other's hand, forming a circle around the hospital bed, *Hail Mary, full of grace, the Lord is with thee; blessed art thou amongst women, and blessed is the fruit of thy womb, Jesus. Holy Mary, Mother of God, pray for us sinners, now and at the hour of our death. Amen.* When the family finished the Lord's prayer, Frances opened her eyes, reached for her mom, and whispered, "I'll be home soon."

CHAPTER SIX

DEANNA

I was dehydrated, hungry, and tired. Scott and I stayed after wrestling practice drilling for the Poway tournament, one of the toughest tournaments in the San Diego county. The last guy I wrestled in the tournament was popped for steroids, but by that time, it was too late for me to advance. I promised myself this would be the year I went to the high school state championships, the first to do it in school history. Leading practice and running miles in a hot suit to cut weight shed its toll, but I had to win. Coach hadn't been much help teaching new techniques, so I would out grind any mother fucker who stood in my way. Pure grit.

Work got in the way, too. I wish I could quit, but I had to buy Shannon the gold chain with a little heart so she would stop bitching that I didn't spend enough time with her. I saved for a month from my job at Sea World selling souvenirs. For her birthday, I placed the chain around her neck as she sat on my lap; she was finally happy. I sprung it on her that I wouldn't be around for the weekend again. She leaped from my lap and walked away. Whatever.

Deanna was always bitching before I walked through the door, something that I had to look forward to every day. There was always some reason: my bed wasn't made; I didn't help my baby brother with his homework; the cats weren't fed; this shit; that shit. I always did something wrong, and she was notorious for pointing it out to me. Every chance I could, I found myself spending the night with Scott or Larry just so I wouldn't have to return home. Hanging with my boys, playing video games, wrestling talk, anything to get my mind off what awaited me.

The day of the Poway tournament, I went through my takedowns: single leg and double leg. My snap down takedown was my secret weapon that I had practiced all season. I drained my ears and sipped water all week to make weight. I didn't eat, which never mattered since Deanna didn't cook. Sometimes, I had no energy to stay up in class, laying my head on my desk while others scribbled their notes, but I knew winning would be worth it despite my academics suffering. When I wrapped my hands around Calderon, I felt his weight too far forward. I faked with my right and came over the top with my hand collar tied. I snapped him down to his face, and he dropped forcefully on the mat. He tried to resist, but I kept the pressure on top of his head. I pulled him towards my lead leg, circled, and snapped. I drove my shot across and scored two points to secure victory as the final seconds ticked. As I stood on the podium, the gold medal was placed around my neck. I wore it on the bus ride back to the Bay and walked home with it around my neck. Before I turned the knob to the front door, I hid the medal in my pocket.

"Where the fuck have you been? You're fucking high and drunk. Aren't you?"

"No, I'm not, mom. I was at a wrestling tournament." I placed the season schedule on the refrigerator door, but Deanna never went to a dual meet.

She rolled her eyes, "Whatever. I don't know why you do that shit. You're no fucking good at it anyways."

I yanked the medal from my pocket, throwing it on the ground, "I placed first." The medal skipped on the wooden floor planting face down. I pushed passed Deanna, slamming my bedroom door. I could hear her bitch even more, so I tossed on my headphones and forced myself to shut my eyes. Even getting decent sleep was difficult in her house. When I finally did, I was woken up by an ice bucket of water to my face or a slap upside my head, "Get up you lazy asshole." I was called everything, but my name, and I responded to it. As a kid, if I came home with broken bones from falling off my skateboard, she'd wrapped her nails around my neck, pinning me against the wall. If I joined the wrestling team, I could defend myself, at least physically.

When I woke up the next day, the medal was gone. I didn't waste my time asking Deanna what she did with it. I didn't care. I forgot to finish my homework again, but I dressed for school anyways. I could copy off Shannon during study hall if she wasn't pissy. I stuffed my wrestling gear into my backpack and rushed out the door without eating breakfast again, avoiding eye contact with Deanna.

I hurried to the wrestling room before school started. Coach gave me the key, trusting me since I was the team captain. The wrestling room was empty. I flipped on the lights, sitting at the center of the mat. I laced my shoes, jogged around the room a few times before stretching. I did jumping jacks, push-ups, crunches, planks, burpees, squats, anything to get stronger. The state tournament was right around the corner. If I placed, it would grab the attention of college recruiters, and I could leave home. There was no other option. I had to prove myself one last time.

CHAPTER SEVEN

DIVORCED PARENTS

My earliest memory of love was my parents arguing in the kitchen right before their divorce. Every night it was something new. Voices shouting at the top of their lungs with veins popping out their necks, like two lions waiting to attack. Who knows what they were arguing about this time. Mommy and daddy standing on opposite sides of the kitchen, mommy to my left, daddy to my right. I couldn't take it any longer, so I stood in the middle, my small frame looking up begging them to stop, but neither parent paid me any mind. So, I stood by mommy, she hugged me, and I screamed for daddy to stop; he didn't. So, I stood by daddy, he hugged me, and I screamed for mommy to stop; she didn't. It was no use; I gave up.

Towards the end, mommy and daddy fought about everything just to fight. One time, they fought over that stupid Aztec picture that's in every Mexican household, the one where the strong Aztec king is caring the helpless Aztec princess, the one that you can buy for a quarter at any *panaderia*. That night, I helped daddy fold his clothes into his briefcase. Mommy held brother on her hip waiting by the door, while daddy packed his car. Before he drove off, he waved at me, and I cried for him to stay, but he left anyways.

For my 4th birthday, daddy bought me a Pac-Man piñata, and mommy dressed me in one of those Mexican dresses that made me itch. My cousins came to my party as well as my best friend, Sam, who lived next door. Sam had all the miniature NFL helmets lined up on a wooden shelf mounted to the wall. He'd help me memorize all the team's names. Other days, he'd come over my house to play Atari or play in the backyard on my swing set. I had a dog named Buster, who cuddled with me when I slept. Before I went to bed, daddy recited my favorite bedtime stories, *Little Red Riding Hood* or the *Three Little Pigs*. He incorporate himself and my uncles into the tales. Tio Rick was the pig that made his house of straw; Uncle Chunky made his house of sticks; and daddy was the clever pig who made his house of bricks. When daddy got to the part where the wolf burnt his *nalgas*, I laughed every time. The night daddy left me all of my childhood memories left with him too.

Neither of my parents remarried. Ralph never brought *another* around me, and Maria had so many boyfriends during the years, I didn't bother to learn their names because they where soon gone. It was the same cycle: bring a man to the house; then he disappeared, leaving Maria in tears, questioning her worth. She'd lock herself in her room, and I heard her sob through the cracks, "No! No! No!" Maria settled for any man that came her way, and she tried her best to keep him, showering him with money, giving him rides, sleeping in her bed. Nothing she did worked until she decided she was better off without.

I accidentally walked in on a drug deal one morning. I rode the trolley over to Ralph's house unexpectedly. He was living in a one bedroom apartment in Chula Vista, and I had the keys to his apartment. When I opened the door, it was chained from the inside, but enough for me to see it all. Ralph was sitting at the dining table with a group of guys making a deal, sorting through the drugs and cash. One guy rolled up hard to the door, "Who the fuck are you?" He flared in my eyes reaching for the pistol in his waist. Ralph quickly came to the door to intervene, peeking through the opening, "I have friends over. You can't come in," his voice trembled as he shut the door. Later that day, he called to explain, but I didn't want to hear another fabricated story.

Needless to say that when I discovered he was diagnosed with AIDS, it didn't surprise me. I was getting ready in the bathroom while Ralph made another run to the liquor store. I shuffled through the drawers and instead of finding my comb, I came across a note stating that he was infected with the AIDS virus. I placed the note back in its place, and I continued getting ready, but I hid the pain for years. When Ralph screamed, as usual, angry at the world, he slapped his face and banged his fist on his head.

"I told you I have AIDS, and you have no reaction!"

I froze, and then responded, "It's about time you confessed."

That night, I yelled into my pillow until I passed out. A witness to hell. His deception turned me into an angry ball of fire —I hardly knew Ralph after that. The drugs and unprotected anal sex continued. Not a fuck in the world from him, just plain old selfish fun with no responsibilities. Go for it. *I'll die anyways* was his philosophy. The hole in my life cultivated with more lies to my face. I might as well been in a coma, at least I could sleep with my eyes closed. Looking in the mirror, all I saw was that same numb little girl as Ralph left me for a second time. But this time, I didn't cry for him to come back.

This was the way I thought it should be. Love that is.

CHAPTER EIGHT

UNJUSTIFIED REACTION

My mind became a shadow,
Clouded with every gray line.
Let me forget this over time,
Don't ever come back to my mind.
Spit these words that speak when you lie.
What are you going to think up this time?

Fool me again, I'll be back for that promise,
Until you are honest
In the modest
Sense of the word,
Turn to the fake life that I heard.

Was this the last? Who am I kidding?
It's another one of your missions completing.

The candle burnt on both ends,
The rain puts it out when the spell sends

You knocking on my door, so I open it.
And you stand there looking in,
But not another myth again
I ain't having it.

Too many stones in this rainbow,
I let go before hitting the ultimate low.
It's too late to debate,
At any rate, it's no longer great,
To see you in my tunnel vision
With such precision.

Warning signs all around,
But you played me for a foolish clown.
That was my fault, holy father.
As a matter of fact, I'll take you farther,
Cuz you were a sinner as a beginner.

Never adapted to change,
The generic face that you made,
From the mistakes you thought would fade,
But they stayed
Permanently
Sunk into my reality
Can't deny my creativity
Pull me up towards gravity
Stop fucking lying to me!

My mind is like a pen,
No running out of ink,
Only makes me think,
Of the embarrassment
No more harassment
What you said instead
As I laid in bed
Wishing I were dead.

Give a fuck next time,
You owe it to your daughter for the first time,
Give up the drinking and drugs from time to time,
I'm almost done with my last rhyme,
But in the meantime,

I will not apologize
I will speak the truth until you realize
It's only fair game when you play
Forgive me, but I refuse to shy away
Can't find my cascade
That I search for every day
Well I don't know what else to say
About this unforgiven disease called AIDS.

CHAPTER NINE

FIRST KISS

My first kiss was from a girl. Maria never allowed boys to call the house let alone going over to his would be considered a sin. I had crushes on boys in my class, but if one came near me, I'd smack him on his head with my lunchbox as a sign of affection.

It was a sleepover for Adeline's birthday. Her living room filled with purple balloons and Red Vines in jars. The theme was Jem. Us, girls, wore pink wigs and sang using a wooden spoon as a microphone. Maria promised she would pick me up first thing in the morning to go to church. Maria already planned for my first communion, traveling down to Tijuana to buy my dress and rosary. I vowed to behave and recite my prayers before I went to bed that night.

After we were done cutting the cake, most of the girls fell asleep watching Alvin and the Chipmunks, but Adeline and I were wide awake. I tucked myself into my sleeping bag. She crept in, pressing her hips against mine. I didn't know what to do at first until she cupped her hands around my butt. I followed her lead, accepting of her physical touch. She slid her tongue around my lips, moist, as I had imagined my first kiss to be, but it didn't come from a boy. She moved her tongue in and out as I closed my eyes picturing the cutest boy in school. Adeline began to rub my privates, and I let her. She crest my shoulders, laying her hand on my back. Her touch was gentle.

This I thought would be the same gentle touch from all men. Taking his time to do things right. What's the hurry? We have all night. I wanted to hold hands in public, cuddle, buy me flowers, take me out to dinner, whisper sweet nothings in my ear. I yearned for sexual passion with my partner, like the one I had with Adeline. Not with my head banging against the headboard with my breast flapping in my face.

He wrapped his hand around my neck, thrusting between my legs. No eye contact. "You need to watch porn to lighten up," he said, "it's not a big deal." He watched it religiously every day. It was always scattered around his dad's house growing up. It helped him through college, taking a mental break when the semester and wrestling season were too hectic. The fantasies he pictured in his head that I obligated to fulfill or else he would find someone who would.

She's 18, at the most, maybe. She walks through a hiking trail, meets a man. Alone. They engage in a few sentences before she's sucking his cock, his pants around his ankles. She sticks her finger in his asshole, pulling her head towards his big dick. She might be on cocaine from what it looks. Her eyes wide open, but his head points to the sky. He orders her to suck harder, so he can nut in her mouth. He lays her on the dirt and drives himself in as she plays with her tits, licking her nipples. He bangs the shit out of her pussy before the juices pour out on both ends, but before he cums, he sticks his dick back in her mouth. He squirts. She swallows.

He didn't move his hips slowly, always in a rush to get it done after a long day at work. No kisses on the neck to get the mood started, "Just stick it in your mouth. Get it wet." He covered my mouth, but I stayed silent anyways. Like the girl in porn, I do what I'm told. I can obey all sorts of commands: lay on my back, turn around, get on top, lift my legs, stroke his penis. Once he was done, he pushed me away, his back turned for the night. He was quickly asleep, snoring. I was left in the dark making sure I didn't cross over to his side of the bed. I thought about my first kiss with Adeline. Her perfectly shaped lips and long brown hair. Her smile and silly dance moves. That one night we had together, and I wonder if somewhere she was thinking about me, too.

CHAPTER TEN

BIG PUTO, LIL' PUTO

Pops called to invite me to this house for the UFC fights. Pops always had a men's night and ordered the UFC fight. It was a tradition with him, my uncles, and a few friends. The guys having fun, drinking beer, and shots of alcohol. Pops already had the Christmas tree up with a few presents for his grandkids wrapped. I was a little late since I was running wrestling practice. During the holiday, I dismissed the boys early so they could spend it with their families. Pops always had a fridge full of beer and a honey baked ham in the oven ready to devour. Pops' Harley was parked in the garage, and I sat on it pretending to ride it like my Pops.

Pops whistled at the card girls circling around in the ring with their tits and asses hanging out their booty shorts. I whistled, too, making Pops proud that I was his boy. Before each bout, we threw in a couple of bucks for shits and giggles to bet on the fighters. I supported my boy, Danny Castillo, who was an old college buddy of mine at Menlo College. When I was sleeping in the locker rooms, Danny opened his place to me even though we didn't get along at the time. We bumped heads many times during practice to see who could be the Alpha wrestler battling until there was only one man left standing. Neither one of us backed down. But when Danny saw me heading into the locker room with my backpack and sleeping bag, we put all that shit aside, and from there, we became brothers.

A sudden knock was at the door in between our hooting and hollering. There stood a lady with big red hair wearing her makeup as if she was stuck in the disco era. She gave us a quick high pitched greeting, and Pops followed her upstairs playfully slapping her ass, raising his glass. We cheered for him like if he won a knockout fight in the final seconds. Kathy was out of town for the weekend, traveling for her salon business that she and her daughter co-owned, and she was gone for a week, plenty of time for Pops to handle his other side pieces. We heard the bed pounding between her moaning. When they were done, the red-headed left without making any eye contact with the rest of us. Pops came back down with a big grin on his face, went to the fridge and cracked open another beer. "That's how you do it, son. These women are all the same. They enjoy their face buried in the sack," he said with joy in this eyes. Pops had a thing for women with big hair, "The bigger the hair the nicer the cunt," he laughed, "make sure you wrap your arms around her neck and show her who's boss when you're banging her." Everyone in the house knew not to ask questions. Pops' arms were as big as his thighs, his long grey hair slicked back in a ponytail. He wore his Santana roofing tank top and dark shades no matter the weather. By the end of the night, Pops stuck the sheets in the washer, spraying the covers with Kathy's lavender perfume. When done, the condom wrapper thrown in the neighbor's trash bin, text messages erased, the evidence gone.

Pops met many women through his roofing business. Since I was a kid, Pops put me to work early, stacking shingles and sweeping all the crud that dropped from the roof. Climbing a ladder and hauling nails and hammers on my belt prepared me for the upcoming wrestling season. Many single women desperately needed a repair in more ways than one. Pops gave them the good old-fashioned Santana discount in exchange if he was able to take them out to dinner, and they always agreed. Sometimes, the women agreed to their discount right there and lead him into their bedroom for the instant Santana discount. How cool to get paid to fuck while on the job. That didn't sound like such a bad deal. When I start my moving company, I could apply the same discounts.

Pops and Kathy had separate kids from separate marriages but never any together. Pops kept his business separate from Kathy, always had play money at his discretion. Kathy never grew suspicious, or maybe she didn't ask questions, or maybe she knew better because she learned her lesson after the first time. From there, Kathy knew her place. A slap to her mouth took care of all future questions. That didn't work with Deanna, though. Pops and Deanna ended their argument with a fist fight competition, Deanna icing her eye and Pops with scratches on his face and neck. I did nothing. As a little boy, all I could do was watch.

CHAPTER ELEVEN

LA MARCHA

He called me the night before and said he wanted more space and would call me when he was ready to see me again. During our time away, I spent it with my family, particularly Uncle Chunky, who shared his stories with me, and I wrote them in my journal to remember my family history.

Uncle Chunky gave me a ring when I arrived home from teaching. He could count on me as his scapegoat, and I instantly swung by his house of chaos. He made up another scenario of meeting a sponsor for an upcoming gig, and they were to settle the logistics in person. Chiquita's was one of those restaurants were everyone either fucked or fought or did both. When Papa Ray was alive, he'd shut down the bar to throw his personal party with trays of tequila and fun women. At the time, I was amongst the underage crowd partaking in the show and free drinks. This was the hangout spot if one yearned for a guaranteed three day hangover.

Rancheras screeched over the speakers, and the Padres were up 2-0 in the 5th inning.

Uncle Chunky wore his signature musical hat with a pearl pinned to its side. He adjusted his scarf, "It's nippy outside." He strutted to his usual spot at the corner of the bar, so he could lean his back against the wall, "I'm here for a quicky, Lorraine."

"But I'm working, babe."

Uncle Chunky released a few chuckles, "Come stick one on Big Daddy." She leaned over the counter for his kiss, "The first one is on the house. Boss' orders." Lorraine was a former bodybuilder turned bartender who rode her Harley to work, her long black hair sank into her leather jacket. She worked jobs in construction, moving, and roofing, could build a house but also crafted jewelry in her spare time. Lorraine flipped the glass, catching it behind her back and dashed a wink at Uncle Chunky as she poured his drink. No matter where he went in San Diego, people lined up to buy him shots. Uncle Chunky raised his glass, blessed the air with the sign of the cross, and toasted, "Here's to the Aztec God of Huitzilopochtli." He wiped his handlebar mustache and danced in his seat after he was done.

"That picture," I pointed, "how old are you?"

A portrait of Uncle Chunky marching alongside Cesar Chavez hung in a frame, "Oh shit. About 300 pounds ago, Veer. I was a spring chicken back then. I was able to walk and do a bunch of other shit." In the picture, Uncle Chunky stood behind Cesar with his signature acoustic guitar.

"Where are you?"

"You asked a bunch of questions even when you were a little girl. Your dad always warned me about it," Uncle Chunky caught Lorraine's attention as a regular stuffed dollar bills down her shirt. "Another stiff one, Sugar Doll," he blew a kiss in the air. "Cesar and I go way back, man. That picture is taken in front of the Campbell's headquarters. Their vegetable soups were contaminated by pesticides. Word on the street spread fast that our people were being taken advantage of by big corporations that had no intention of helping us. As long as we give them our money, that's all that mattered. Green is green, *que no?*" Cesar got wind of the news and requested Los Alacranes to join him on the 500-mile march from Ohio all the way to the headquarters in New Jersey. I packed my guitar and a few belongings. I put some miles on the feet," Uncle Chunky made an effort to wiggle his toes. "We made flyers and passed them out at schools or community events. The news didn't cover much of the story, hiding the political agenda for the profits of people. We had to create scandals."

Uncle Chunky was one of thirty original marchers who completed the entire distance of the march, although protesters faded in and out. There were challenges along the way, blisters, torn shoes, not enough food or supplies, but people stepped up for the cause. A football player from the Pittsburg Steelers purchased new shoes for the marchers, and along the way, people opened up their homes. "One lady let us shower and served us beans, the Mexican version of steroids. A big pot sizzled on the stove. I chowed down on ten bowls that day. It reminded me of my mom's cooking. I asked the lady who showed her how to cook. She said it was her mom's secret recipe. Her mom owned restaurants in Sinaloa, and her beans were the hottest ticket on the menu. That was enough to keep us going."

As the distanced prolonged, people weakened, including Cesar. "We told Cesar he didn't have to march all the way, but he did. I walked alongside him playing *huelga* songs. *United with Cesar Chavez, no les moveran. United with the people, we shall not be moved. Just like a tree standing by the river. No les moveran.*"

A chapel in the outskirts of town arranged for thirty priests to wash the feet of the original marchers. "I could feel the gravel on my soles. There were times when I would call it quits until we reached the church." The marchers were seated at the altar, each priest bringing a basin filled with holy water to soak their feet. They kneeled to Cesar and his people, presenting them with the body of Christ for the journey ahead. The priests blessed the people, praying that they stood strong. "When Cesar arrived in New Jersey, he had someone on each side holding him up. We formed a pathway for him that lead to the stairs of the headquarters, and as he passed, we bowed our heads. It was a long ways to go, but we finished."

Uncle Chunky and I were the last ones at the bar. Waitresses placed chairs upside down on the tables, customers paid their tab, and lights began to dim. Lorraine was stocking the bar for the day shift.

"You ready to go home, Veer?"

"Nah. You?"

"Let's grab one more before we hit the road." And we waited at the bar until time ran out.

I never fully comprehended the meaning when Ralph called to report that Cesar Chavez had died.

"Do you know who he is?"

"Yes, the boxer," I joked. Ralph had to persuade Maria to let me skip school. I don't know how he convinced her since she was strict about my studies, but whatever he said worked. Tio Rick rented a sixteen-passenger van where all the cousins squeezed in for the trip to Delano. Tio Rick always drove, and Uncle Chunky was co-pilot. Their instruments were loaded in the back. We packed snacks and water to get us through the trip. I was twelve.

When we arrived, mourners crowded the streets, and the news anchors interviewed Hollywood actors, like Paul Rodriguez. My uncles began tuning their guitars, clearing their throats to loosen their vocals. There were children younger than me caring the UFW flags. I found one and carried it throughout the five-mile march. I mingled in a crowd that chanted, *"Viva Cesar Chavez!" "Viva La Huega!" "Si Se Puede!"* Tata was alive at the time, and he marched every step of the way. Tata was from Sinaloa and crossed over to the states picking watermelon in the fields of Blythe, where he raised four kids. My uncles and dad worked in the fields as teenagers, but it wasn't something they planned for the rest of their lives, so they migrated to San Diego, carrying their guitars and stories with them. Tata retired as a farmer, never missed work, while Nana stayed home cooking packing lunches, and scrubbing floors while everyone was away.

I followed the crowd, separating from my family. Even though the heat stuck to my skin, I kept marching, each step planted in history. Some people chanted, others prayed, others sang along. When I arrived at the final destination, mourners were lined up for the viewing, placing roses on Cesar's casket. People were crying but proud at the same time. Although too young at the time, I realized my life changed that day. It was my first of many marches. I began reading more on Cesar and the labor unions. I wrote book reports, gave school presentations, showing my UFW flag. A part of history that I can pass down to my children. I was there with Cesar leading the way one last time.

CHAPTER TWELVE

SIBLING LOVE

Tio Rick and Uncle Chunky tuned their guitars outside Tio Rick's apartment to prepare for their upcoming gig for the Chicano Park celebration. Already a few drinks deep, a Bloody Mary and a pint of Christian Brothers Brandy were key ingredients to opening up their vocal cords and relaxing their fine muscles. This was an Alacran ritual for the past forty years, and it was never skipped.

"Are you going to play in the right key this time?" Uncle Chunky sarcastically asked his brother.

"Only if you sing the song right. It's not fucking hard to sing a *corrido*. They all sound the same."

"I'm the one doing all the singing and all the work. Sometimes I forget, man."

"You don't forget to sign autographs and take pictures with everyone in the world during Chicano Park Day. The Chicano Park Steering Committee should just stick you in a tent like Santa Claus, so people can sit on your lap and take pictures of you all day."

"You're a big complaining grouch, Rick."

"Is Armpits going to be there?" Tio Rick laughed at his own jokes before taking a drink of his Bloody Mary, "Her fucking armpit hairs look like they fight with each other. Fucking braids hanging under her arms. She grosses me out even from the back side. I know she's your sister-in-law, but she's nasty."

"That's cold blooded. Don't say that in front of my old lady or else I'll never hear the end of it."

"What's she going to do about it? You're the one she and OLE cursed."

Just then, Ralph busted through the gate pounding his cane with every stagger, but even with the help of the cane, he galloped off balance, leaning to one side. Over the years, Ralph fell so many times, mathematicians can't come up with a number high enough for the equation. For my baptism, Ralph ordered five kegs, which is about average for your typical Mexican religious ceremony. By the middle of the party, he did a summersault into the splits, which didn't turn out too graceful resulting in one of several sprained ankles.

"Virgie's right behind me, and she's in a bad mood. We made a stop at McDonald's. She ordered two egg McMuffins, one donut, and three pancakes that she ate on the drive here," Ralph said waving his cane in the air, "she cussed fifty seven times. I counted."

"Ralph, we're trying to get a song list ready for Chicano Park. Don't get in our way."

"Ha!" Ralph shouted as he pulled out a plastic bottle of vodka from his sagging shorts, "I don't know why you're practicing. You guys play the same boring shit every year. I beg you, please don't sing *De Colores* again for the hundredth time. I'm sick of hearing it. It's like the Mexican version of *We Shall Overcome*."

"That's an important traditional song. We played that song for marches with Cesar and Corky."

"The Chicano movement ended in the 70's, Ray. Get over it, and play something new." Ralph said referring to his brother by his English name.

"We're playing *Jarochas*, too."

"*Jarocha la panocha*, right Ray," Ralph said slapping his brother on his back, "speaking of pussies is Betty going to run out the Miller Lite girls again? *Viejas cochinas*! *Nasty women*!" Ralph shouted spitting in Uncle Chunky's face. During one of the celebrations, the Miller Lite girls asked for a picture with Uncle Chunky, but instead, they were met by his wife, the witch, who ran them off screaming insults. The Miller Lite girls, not to be outdone, lifted their already see through tops, flashing their chi-chis in the witch's face and bouncing up and down in the process. For the first time in her life, the witch was speechless.

"My old lady gets mad when you don't say hi to her."

"Do I give a husky fuck? I can't see her anyways because she blends in with the dirt."

"Just say hi to her so I don't get in trouble."

"Ray, the last time we spoke to each other we only said two words: fuck you and shut up."

"Doesn't it look like Virgie was drafted as an offensive lineman by the Chargers?" Rick whispered as their sister made her way out of her car. He made a fist with a small hole where he blew pretending to be a sports announcer, "And coming in, weighing 350 lbs, the San Diego Chargers first round pick, Virginia Zarp."

"I heard that, asshole. Rick, you do have a shirt that covers your fat stomach? You shop in the Samoan section at K-Mart, and you still can't find a decent shirt that fits you."

"Well, I don't want to brag, but I'm the best dressed here." Ralph was dressed in a Madonna t-shirt, shorts with the stem unthreading from the back pocket, one black ankle sock, one blue knee sock, and a bleached stained sweater dropped over his back, like if he was playing golf. All clothes purchased at a yard sale for one dollar, total.

"My mom raised three fucked up sons." Aunt Virgie said eating the last bite of her egg McMuffin, "Where was her logic? You three are the biggest fuck ups in the world. Mother should've stopped having kids after me. I'm the only normal one."

"I'll take you to McDonald's again if you stop PMSing. Just remember, they don't serve burgers for breakfast."

"Shows what you know, idiot. I haven't had a period in over fifteen fucking years."

"I'm the smartest one in the family, Virgie. I have a master's degree," Ralph bragged again placing his hand on his hip, giving her a smirk.

"Yeah, you're also the poorest. You eat out of a can of beans that you get free from all food banks around town."

"Virgie, you're in no position to give nutrition advice."

"I may be fat, but at least I'm not poor. I don't have to rely on the Money Tree to get me through the month. I really hate to sound like a republican, but poverty is a choice. You fuckers are the reasons republicans vote the way they do, and I don't blame them."

"I'm not going to invite you to anymore of my parties, Virgie, because trays of food come up missing."

"I paid for the food, so it's mine. You made my life difficult for your 60th birthday party. I'm never doing anything for you again. If you ever die, I'll plan that party because you'll be dead, and you won't have shit to say."

"Speaking of missing things, Chilli found your teeth again, Ralph." Tio Rick said as he handed Ralph a plastic bag that was in his pocket.

"Oh really? Where were they this time?"

"In between the couch cushions."

"And there ain't a bump in my gums," Ralph smiled sticking his dentures back in his mouth, "how do my teeth look?"

"Why is there a bone sticking out of your ankle?" Uncle Chunky noticed instead.

"I fell."

"Where?"

"Tijuana."

"Let me guess? Falling crossing the bridge on another one of your *borracheras*. You pack a year of drinking into one night. You act just like dad. My brothers come from a long line of fucked up men. I'm just thankful your driver's license was suspended indefinite. You can't drink and drive like you use to. You hit cars, poles, trees, houses, animals. I never did stupid shit like that even when I was young and sober."

"I made it safe to the other side, okay. That's all that matters. You couldn't run around the block if your life depended on it. Women aren't supposed to walk like construction workers or astronauts."

"I don't need to walk when I can afford a vehicle. Besides, you're in no fine shape yourself. You still have Kaiser? You still on that preventative coverage shit because you're too fucked up to take care of yourself."

"Virgie, I have a disability."

"Yeah, it's called being a male. I don't know what the fuck is wrong with your gender. They can't seem to keep their dicks in their pants."

"The *viejas* have to keep their legs closed, too."

"We're all fat and fucked up, Ralph," Tio Rick intervened as he poured himself another drink.

"Some more than others," Ralph winked at Tio Rick gesturing towards his sister, "Virgie, do you still wear a 6X?"

"I least I can say I've never been mistaken for a homeless person. Do you still have fleas and scabies living on you? I can never tell if you're loaded because you look miserable all the time. Most people don't know you drink until they see you sober."

"Can we focus back on our song list? I have to leave soon to go pick up dinner for my old lady."

"Tell her to fuck off," Aunt Virgie kindly suggested, "she reminds me of the rhyme the old lady who lived in a shoe. She had so many kids. She didn't know what to do."

"Betty doesn't give a shit about 95% of your life anyways, unless she's clipping money from our gigs."

"Ray, you need to get a haircut before Chicano Park. You look like the cowardly lion from the Wizard of Oz. You need that red bow tied in your hair, so you look nice for the *viejas cochinas*. Oops, I mean the Miller Lite girls."

"You look like Papa Smurf with your nasty beard. I'll pay you to shave it off."

"Rick, you're so black you're purple."

"And top that with your charming Indian personality. You can hold grudges forever, and you're cheap. For Christ's sake, you're too cheap to pay to get into Chilli's football games, so you hide behind the fences and trees. You sit in the back just so you drink your Goddamn booze."

"You might be pleasant to talk with one of these days if you didn't cuss like a sailor."

"Yeah, Virgie. Everyone's not rich like you," Ralph added emptying the last of his vodka down his throat.

"The game cost $7 for Christ's sake."

"You guys are making me want to drink more," Uncle Chunky raised his bottle in the air, "here's to the Aztec God of Huit..."

"Chunky, shut up," Tio Rick interrupted, "you don't need to make a fucking announcement every time you take a fucking drink."

"I need to go soon, man."

"Ray, you just need to file for divorce. I'll help you. I don't care who the guy is. I'm always on his side when he gets a divorce, Arnold Schwarzenegger, Ike Turner, all of them."

"See what I mean. My brothers are so fucked up Dr. Phil couldn't help you, morons."

"I'll be on Bill's side when he divorces you."

"Fuck you and the horse you rode on."

"Virgie, come give Big Daddy a hug."

"I really don't want to say this because you guys are my brothers, but I hate you," Aunt Virgie said as she flipped off her brothers, and they laughed even more, taking jabs, everyone getting their fair dose of sibling love.

CHAPTER THIRTEEN

CHOLULA

As I laid alone in bed again, I wrote a story in my journal that Uncle Chunky shared using as a distraction instead of thinking about my boyfriend and his whereabouts. I was at Aunt Virgie's house for dinner, and Uncle Chunky stopped by to drop off the chairs he borrowed for the witch's party. Bill knew Uncle Chunky's ritual and poured him a shot of brandy imported from France that he bought at Trader Joe's. The alcohol must've reminded Uncle Chunky about his search for alcohol in Cholula.

"Chunky! Who let you backstage, carnal?"

"Kick back, Cesar. El Chunky has a way with the ladies. I still got it like that, man," the two friends hugged, "it's been awhile. That was a nice set you played."

"Going back to our roots."

"You got down on the acoustics. Not bad for a *vato* from East L.A." Chunky and Cesar developed quite the relationship over the decades. Before they were well-known Grammy artist, Los Lobos jammed with Los Alacranes in the backyard of the red house, where Chunky's parents lived. The groups performed for a few cases of beer and gas money for the ride home. Fita fed her sons and the rest of the party with pots of beans and homemade tortillas, kids jumped on the trampoline, empty kegs, runs to the liquor store, underwear from both men and women flying the air, and the music gathered the family together. The parties lasting for a few days.

"Want a shot for old times' sake?"

"Why are you even asking?" Cesar signaled to one of the crew members for the drinks.

"Remember the ANGF Conference in Cholula?"

"Oh boy, oh boy. That's where we met, *que no*?"

"I learned to play my first *Jarocho* there. Our instructor was an old cat from Xalapa. His hands were like concrete. I hadn't developed the callous on my fingers yet, and he called me a *panocha*, a pussy, said I was soft." Cesar raised his hands, "We've come a long way from our radical days. If our hands could tell a story."

"That's some scandal right there. Remember Teno? Whatever happened to him?"

Cesar laughed with hesitation, "The witch's dust."

"Com'on man. That might not be true."

"I don't know, brother. How's your curse coming along?"

"Jive sucker." The shots arrived on a ceramic tray. Chunky and Cesar reached for the tequila.

"You know the routine, Chunky."

"To Cholula."

ANFG is a conference where dancers and musicians come for a week to learn the traditional art of music and dance directed by the best instructors in Mexico. At the end of the week, students perform what they learned, keeping culture alive. However, this particular conference week took place during election day. It *should* be impossible to find alcohol since the entire country *should* be dry. Impossible is only a word until someone achieves it.

With no plan in mind, Chunky, Cesar, and Teno boarded a bus that hauled caged chickens and goats, some inside and some propped on the roof. The bus was lit with candles and pictures of every saint known to Catholicism stuck to the windows. It reminded Chunky of his mother's alter. "I don't know whether to kneel down and pray or get off. Better red than dead," Chunky said with a cynical laugh as he did the sign of the cross. The bus driver, a bald sun-bronzed man with goggles, collected the passengers' pesos and placed the coins in the pocket of his *guayabera*. The seats were upside down paint buckets loosely glued to the floor. The bus travel down a dirt road into a small pueblo. The cars they passed were abandoned with stray dogs curled underneath for shelter. Clouds began to turn gray as the sun hid underneath the earth, and the moon began making its debut into the rattling sky. When the bus arrived at its final destination, it parked near a waterfront bar with broken windows that reeked of piss mingled with illegal smoke. The *panaderia* and *helado* carts were shut down for the night, business lights flickered, and a white-haired lady wrapped herself in a *zarape* as she hugged herself to sleep on a park bench.

"*Jefe,*" Chunky turned to the bus driver as he stepped off, "*donde puedemos encontrar unos tragos?*" The bus driver pointed down the street to where they could acquire liquor, then quickly peeled away, leaving a trail of dust in the air.

"Well that wasn't much help," Cesar coughed as he removed his signature sunglasses rubbing his eyes and placing them back on his face.

"Are you gonna take those off? It's dark now."

"How else would you recognize my pretty face, ese?"

"You look like one of the three blind mice."

"When's the last time your Indian ass showered? Five thousand years ago when *Aztlán* was built? That smells about right."

"Jive suckers. Come to your senses, man. We're here to serve a greater purpose," Chunky announced. They continued down the street bumping into a few stragglers until they came across a ranchero with long hair sitting on a tree stump. He dressed in a shirt with holes in the armpits and wore elastic sandals a few sizes too small.

"*Señor, cuanto nos falta para llegar a pistiar.*" The ranchero sparked a cigarette and looked Chunky up and down.

"*Me gustan tus zapatos,*" the ranchero commented on Chunky's shoes as he inhaled a puff. Chunky, getting the hint, untied his shoes, handing them to the ranchero, "*y tu bandera,*" he eyeballed Teno's Azteca bandana, and Teno did the same, "*y los lentes.*"

"No, no, I have to draw the line."

"Give him your sunglasses. You can buy new ones."

"It's not the same. They're my first pair. I bought them before I bought my first guitar."

"I'll buy you a cupcake when we get back to the hotel. We're desperate."

"I don't care."

"You should've listen to me when I told you to take them off back at the bus, *pendejo*."

"Stop acting like my *pinche suegra*."

"I'm not that ugly, brother. But be thankful you're not married to Chunky's mother-in-law. Now, that's the *bruja* of all *brujas*. Remember when she cursed you on your wedding day?"

"That's cold blooded, man. Why do you have to bring that up?"

"That's not cold. It's the truth. Old Lady Enrique sprinkled powder on your head and yelled *que no tienes huevos*. You have no balls."

"One day, OLE will curse your balls, mother fucker. Don't forget she's your dance instructor. You're not off the hook either." The ranchero laughed exposing a two-inch gap in his mouth.

"You can always give homeboy your teeth, Cesar," Teno uttered sarcastically.

"How do we know he's not playing us for some fools? I'm from East L.A. Shit like this happens all the time."

"*Como chingán,*" the ranchero said as he stood from the tree stump amused by their humor, "*sígueme.*"

The ranchero lead them a few miles to the outskirts of town to a rustic house with a tarp roof. A small rectangle window was carved on the front door. Chunky approached the window and knocked with hesitation. The window slowly stretched opened, and the copper eyes of an Indian boy stared back.

"*¿Que quieres?*"

The ranchero stepped in front of Chunky, "*Están conmigo.*"

"*Tres tequilas,*" Chunky slipped the money through the window, and the Indian boy shut the window, returning with shots.

"No lime or salt," Teno complained.

"For an Indian, you sure are picky. Be thankful we have that, jive sucker."

"*Los lentes,*" the ranchero stuck out his hand asking for the shades.

Cesar sighed, and Teno smirked, "Who's the idiot, now?" Cesar clinched his sunglasses, and the ranchero snatched them, hooking the shades on his ears, as he wandered away in style.

Chunky, Cesar, and Teno posted at a round table outside the house. Chunky and Cesar talked about music, songs they wrote, and the dream of getting paid to perform, and Teno reminisced about his war days. For every shot they chugged, they toasted to the city of Cholula for opening her home to strangers, a land of refulgent narratives waiting to be shared with family and friends on the other side of the fence. Dawn burned the morning aura, and roosters echoed in the distance. Wives blazed their stoves boiling rice as their husbands strapped their boots to begin another twelve-hour day hustling at work. The sweet bread and ice cream carts resumed for business, and the white-hair lady who slept on the park bench arranged her handmade Mexican dolls and jewelry on her colorful blanket ready to sell at the tourist who crossed her path.

"*Hijole*, have we been here that long?" Chunky asked as he looked that the pile of shot glasses on the table, "Teno, don't you have to perform today?"

"Fuck!" Teno tried to gain his balance, but he stumbled back in his chair.

Chunky and Cesar lifted Teno, strapping his arms around their shoulders. Luckily for them, a carpenter who was driving to work, spotted the *borracheros*, the drunks, and offered them a ride in his pickup truck since he was going in the same direction. Chunky tossed Teno in the back, who landed face first on bed, his head hitting the carpenter's toolbox. Teno stayed face down all the ride back to the hotel, where he was scheduled to perform *La Danza de los Voladores*, Dance of the Flyers, where Teno must climb a 100-foot pole. Once reaching the top, he would need to fling himself backwards in the air with only a rope tied to his feet. A precious, ancient ritual passed down for centuries to pray to the Gods, until Teno fucked it up.

As the carpenter pulled up to the hotel, OLE was waiting with her bag of tricks.

"Chunky, what is your *suegra* doing here?"

"How am I supposed to know? I thought we left her wrinkled ass back home." Teno rolled over to his back, and Chunky and Cesar plopped him up, escorting him out of the truck. Somehow, Teno was missing a shoe and drool spilled from his lips staining his shirt. His eyes rolled to the side, his words difficult to enunciate.

"I knew you'd be up to no good. Out all night, like a bunch of drunks." OLE criticized as she approached Teno, scenting his odor, "You're not going anywhere. Get on that pole and perform right now. Don't embarrass me. Do you hear me?"

"I hear you, bitch," Teno slurred his words, "did you ride here on your fucking broom?"

"What did you say? *Hombres mugrosos.* You gross men," OLE reached for her bag, but Teno, with perfect timing, let out a tequila fart that smelled like he shitted in his pants, "what did you just do?" OLE plugged her nose.

"Nothing OLE, I mean, *suegra.* Cesar and I will make sure he is ready to go."

"He has thirty minutes to get ready. Mark my words you will be sorry. All of you." OLE murmured something in an unfamiliar language and left still holding her breath.

"I thought Dorothy melted that fucking bitch," Teno said as he was carried to the elevator and up to his room.

Outside the room, the carnival was underway in the streets. Azteca dancers burned sage, kids ran to the cotton candy machine, vendors sold gold fish, and a clown tied balloons into farm animals. The performers where ready to hit the stage, but they waited for Teno, who wiggled his way through the crowd, knocking down a few kids in the process, Chunky and Cesar following behind.

As Teno reached the base of the pole, OLE appeared from behind, pitching his arm, "You're a *sin vergüenza.*"

"I don't have any shame, *panocha vieja.*"

Teno followed the three performers up the pole. Teno was the last to reach the top. He tied the rope around his foot. Once the group reached the top, all four students were supposed to fly back in sync, rotating the direction of the sun. However, not in this case. Teno became dizzy, turning blue, and before he could climb back down, it was too late. The other pole flyers released themselves, taking Teno with them. As they spun in a circle, Teno shook the pole off balance, and that's when he released a night's worth of vomit to the mob below. Chunks spewed in hair, hot dogs, shoes, eyes, you name it. The herd scattered covering themselves like if a flock of seagulls shitted all at once. Once Teno reached the ground, he forgot to pull himself up to untie the rope from his feet. His head dragged along the ground, his face hitting rock after rock, scraping his cheek each time.

"Should we pretend we don't know him and go back to the room?" Chunky suggested.

"OLE will cast a spell on him for sure."

"Maybe people will think he threw up because he's nervous."

"Nobody's that stupid."

A vendor sprinted to Teno, untying the rope from his feet. Others came to assist Teno, but he just laid on the ground covered in his vomit.

"*Mira no mas. Este hombre no sabe portar,*" OLE cried, "why don't you know how to behave when you're in another country?"

Cesar laughed, "Shit, he doesn't know how to behave in any country. Wherever he goes he's known as the town's drunk." OLE reached for her bag and poured dust on Teno's head chanting more gibberish.

"Shit. Let's get the fuck out of here." Chunky and Cesar ran back to the room and locked the door. They could still hear the chaos outside.

To this day, it is unknown what happened to Teno and his dancing career.

"I never saw Teno again after that day."

"Me neither, Chunky. That was a powerful curse."

"Who knows? Who knows, man? Crazy times, brother." Chunky and Cesar raised their glasses with a final salute to Cholula before going their separate ways to realize that Cholula was only a memory, a memory they hadn't thought about in years.

CHAPTER FOURTEEN

LARRY

I met Larry when he was 14 years old the summer before entering our freshman year of high school at the Bay. I never wanted to stay home, so I scraped enough money from my coin jar to purchase a skateboard at the thrift store, even negotiated with the manager who knocked down a few bucks because I was a local PB kid. On my first trip to the bowl, Larry was showing off his sick ass ollies, flipping his board, perfectly timing his landings. Larry weighed a buck ten and wore baggy clothes. I was new to the skating scene, which was probably obvious since I didn't know anyone there. Larry was the first one to talk to me, "So I see you're a newbie, bro. Don't worry, homie. We were all there at one time or another. You'll get the hang of it." After skating at the bowl, Larry invited me to his pad. He lived on the boardwalk in a one bedroom shack with his mother, who was a nurse that worked the graveyard shifts. As a child, Larry spent his days up and down the boardwalk skating, biking, rollerblading, rode anything with wheels, "I love the outdoors, bro," he said as he tossed me a can of Cola, "are you going to the Bay?"

"Yeah, dude. I'm going to join the wrestling team. You should try out."

"No thanks, man. Not my style. I'd rather spend my time by the ocean," Larry cracked open his soda, "you hungry, bro?"

"I can go for a snack."

"I know all the spots in North PB that have fruit trees." We skated up Mission Beach Blvd into the homes of doctors and professional athletes stuffing our pockets with as many fruits as we could. Larry shared his dream of turning pro as we sat on the curb peeling our oranges, "I saw Tony Hawk at the X-Games, and I knew that would be my calling. I wanted to be him. I can get sponsors and eventually buy my mom her dream house."

The rest of summer, I chilled at Larry's pad staying up all night playing video games. He fixed my board, tightening the wheels and decorating it with bumper stickers he had laying around his house. I introduced him to Scott, and the three us of hung out all summer. Scott and I wrestled in the living room, preparing for tryouts while Larry laughed at us. We were boys being boys, knocking over furniture, seeing who could fart the loudest, eating fish tacos, catcalling older chicks who passed even though we didn't stand a chance with them.

Larry wouldn't hurt a fly, so it blew my mind when I received the call from Scott in the middle of the night, "Dude, Larry got jumped by CJ and his baseball crew. It's fucking bad. Really fucking bad." I jumped out of bed and grabbed my board that was always next to my bed. Deanna never cared where I was anyways, assuming I was up to no good. I skated as fast as I could, my heart racing as I ran through red lights and dodged cars. Cars honked their horns, and pedestrians shouted for me to slow the fuck down. When I finally arrived, which seemed like an eternity, Larry's face was covered in an icepack. He slowly removed the pack, both eyes were so swollen he couldn't open them. Blood poured from the open gashes on his forehead, his clothes torn, and his front teeth missing. Scott was already there when I arrived, and Larry's mother was on her way home.

Larry was at a party with the rest of the Bay heads. During the wrestling season, Scott and I kept it low key and stayed home to train the next morning. Earlier, I told Larry I had a funny feeling about the party, but he went regardless. Those stupid high school rumors spread quickly. A chick, Kim, was sprung on Larry, but he wasn't feeling her, even let her down politely. She got in a pissy fit and told the baseball crew he hit her. If anyone knew Larry, they would know that bitch was lying, but Kim was one of the few rich kids at the Bay, the privilege who got away with everything and threw a fit when she didn't get what she wanted. It was a chickenshit move on CJ's part. "He hit me with his cast when I was in the keg line ready to pour my beer. He smacked my head. I tried to get up and run. I heard gunshots. I thought I was dead, bro." There were always those bad seeds at the Bay. The wanna-be hard asses from Linda Vista. They lived in two-story houses, always had a warm meal waiting for them when they arrived home from practice, both parents happily married, private tutors, all that luxury horseshit. They never fought one-on-one. Cowards usually don't. Coach Pugh would cover for them always, much like when he altered their grades so the top players were eligible for baseball season. Baseball players could get away with murder, and they did. The team was ranked #1 in the state of California and #3 in the nation. Our school gym covered with years of the Western League, C.I.F., and state banners. Larry didn't stand a chance. I felt guilty inside. If Scott and I had been there, this shit wouldn't go down.

When Larry's mother arrived, she was already crying. Her only child beaten. She pulled out pain medication from her purse and began cleaning his wounds. Nothing would please me more than to kick the ever loving shit out of CJ and the rest of his bitch ass douchebag crew. "Don't do it. You're about to graduate and wrestle in college, homie." Larry wasn't the first or last one they jumped. They jumped someone every weekend, someone by themselves, someone defenseless. Everyone on campus knew, but everyone kept their mouths shut. Larry was never the same after that. Never right in the head. He'd say off the wall things like, "I don't belong anymore. I don't fit in this world."

I was relieved when Larry met his new chick because it helped him out of his depression, and he was smiling again. He was sprung, showing up at her doorstep every morning with fresh flowers he picked or homemade fruit baskets. In a few months of dating, Larry packed up his bags and moved to South Lake Tahoe. Sold his skateboard and all his other toys, "I don't need it anymore. I'm going to start my life with Quinn. We want to have kids. I'm going to be the best father," Larry promised with joy in his voice. He wanted to name his firstborn, Oasis.

Larry and I kept contact while I was away at Menlo College. When I returned to San Diego, he visited a couple of times. We cruised down the boardwalk for old times' sake. stopping by his old pad. "Those were the days, bro," Larry reminisced as he posted on the boardwalk. Larry planned to propose to Quinn when he returned to South Lake Tahoe. He bought a custom-made silver ring shaped like a wave. "Quinn is pregnant. We tried for years, and it finally happened. You're the first one to know."

Larry returned home ahead of schedule, an unfamiliar car parked in the driveway. He pressed his ear against the door, hearing the fuck noises. He turned the knob slowly and caught Quinn riding some dude's dick. Unlike most people, Larry didn't cause a scene, just left the ring on the coffee table, closing the door behind him. That night, Larry stayed in a motel. He wrote a letter to his mom, and when he was done, he tightened the rope. The motel manager found Larry with his neck cocked back, his feet dragging on the ground. Scott cruised by my pad to break the news. "Fuck!" I slammed my fist on the kitchen counter so hard my bones shattered. I kicked the walls, punched the air, threw shit, feeling the world in the pit of my stomach. I reached for a bottle of hard liquor that I stashed in my cabinet, a bottle always near just in case. I chugged it, and when I was done, I chugged another bottle. I swallowed pills once the bottles were empty. I fumbled into my bed, passing out face down, and I repeated that night for years to come.

CHAPTER FIFTEEN

EASTER

I found a picture of cousin Nando and I sitting on the porch of the red house, flashing our plastic Easter baskets at the camera lens, dressed in something our parents picked out, me in a black and white polka-dot dress with lacy socks and Nando in a button up shirt tucked into his shorts, delicate smiles, not a worry in the glass sky, not a responsibility to oversee our sanity, not a fight to battle, not a devil crawling into our birth rights, only smiles floating on our chocolate faces, and long we sat on the porch of the red house, giggling with innocents, painted hugs tickling to the ground, hearts like caged birds tapping to the Mexican hat dance, lifting our sounds as we catch ourselves once more before we disappear under the earth—separately.

CHAPTER SIXTEEN
A BEATING OR TWO

The first time it happened, I didn't even cry. There was no time. I held my face, my glasses launching five feet in front of me. The blood spilled from my lip, and I whispered, "You hit me." For a moment, I stopped breathing, and I waited for his heavy hand to smack the side of my face again. The blind side of his fist caught me off guard. Rule number one in boxing: never let your hands down. And I failed rule number one.

"Stop being such a fucking baby! Wahh, wahh! Crying like you always do! Wahh, wahh!" His breath spit of cheap vodka, his eyes flaming like fire.

The pressure from his hand grew hotter as he showed me who was boss before slamming the door to our bedroom, cursing through the walls. The couch was becoming all too familiar, my new bed for Zach and I, hugging him as we both shivered in the dark, my hands resting on his paws. I told myself he would sleep it off, wake up, and admit that he would never strike me again. At least Ike bought Tina flowers and clothes after her beatings, easing the pain.

Something for me to say, "Okay. He really didn't mean it this time." There was nothing.

Who knew I could take a punch, just like the women before and after me. Mothers that were beaten and turned to drugs for an outlet. Sinking into a deep hole, abandoning their children. I was no different. I represented a long line of punching bags. The stories on the news of women kidnapped or found dead. I once read about a girl who was murdered on a college campus by a stalker. I shared the article with my college students, and some girls began to cry. I knew the feeling. One student shared her abuse in her class essay. How her boyfriend dragged her down the stairs by her hair and although she kicked and screamed her hardest, she couldn't pull away. I thought it was so easy to get up and leave, but I chose not to because being alone was scarier.

I became proficient at dodging objects thrown my way, whether it was his steaming hot coffee mug, a 35-inch television, or other random objects. When I tried to lock myself in the room, he punched a hole sticking his head through it, like Jack Nicholson in the *Shining* as I curled myself into the fetus position when he entered.

I was another domestic abuse statistic.

In elementary school, I persuaded Ralph to buy me a pair of Jordan's for Christmas. I was ashamed of the Payless Pro Wings, the only shoes Maria could afford. I hid my feet under my school desk praying the other kids didn't take notice, but that was short lived as they pointed at my feet in amusement. I promised Ralph my Jordan's could be a combination of my Christmas and birthday present, seeing my birthday was only a month and a half after Christmas. It would be cheaper this way, I begged. When I want something, I can be pretty convincing. The day after I unwrapped my Jordan's, I marched my happy ass to the basketball court with the rest of the boys. "Get out of here. No girls allowed." This time I refused to listen. I stayed on the court and played. Daniel McQueen attempted to snatch the basketball from me as I dribbled, but I knocked him to the ground. I stood over him as the teacher's aide ran to the court, the rest of the boys huddling around him with wide eyes. Daniel clutched his arm and rolled over to his side. The next day, he showed up to school with a cast. From there on, no boy dared to kick me off the basketball court.

One night, I heard voices arguing outside my living room window. A boy, who looked like he was in high school, roughed up his girlfriend. "You fucked around on me with that Mexican nigga," he screamed in her face. She cried on the street curb weeping as he continued his rant. The arguing occurred for several minutes before I stepped outside, "Get away from her. Leave her alone," I shouted back. His boy waited in a car in the middle of the street, convincing him to get in so they could leave. "Listen to your friend. He's smart enough to take you away. Get in the car and leave." The car door swung opened, and he made his way to the passenger side, slamming the door. He rolled down the window and cursed at her as the car sped down the street. Once the car was out of sight, the girl thanked me in a swollen voice and took off running in the opposite direction.

I walked back inside my house, the lights dim and quiet for now before he arrived from work. As I reached the door, I turned to the empty streets settled into the dark. I gently closed the door to resume in my thoughts. I could save the life of a stranger but not my own, tell her boyfriend to get away and leave, but I stayed quiet with mine. She ran away, and I stayed home. *I wasn't worth saving,* I reminded myself. That's usually how the story goes.

CHAPTER SEVENTEEN

FUNCTIONING DRUNK

This was the last shit I want to hear after a fucked up day at work. My boss continued to spy on my ass making sure I was at my post when school administration was on campus. We now had weekly meetings reviewing security procedures where we were bitched at for not following proper procedures. Layton had me stand in the back of the school by the football field in case any of the students ditch, but honestly, I didn't give a flying fuck. Their parents paid for their education, and it wasn't my money wasted down the drain. I had other shit on my mind, like how was I going to afford to feed another mouth. Maybe I could convince Vera not to keep it. Her timing was always perfect. I had to prepare my guys for the CIF tournament, and this was the shit she dropped on me. She was delusional if she expected a jolly response. Most women are.

After practice, I cruised to the liquor store where they know my name and order now: a fifth of the cheapest vodka, $9.99 a bottle. Before I went inside the house, I popped a few Somas that I hid in the glove compartment. If I ever brought them in the house, her nosey ass would find them, so it was best if I keep them in my car for safety. I stayed in my car for awhile taking my sweet time to head inside. If there wasn't more bad news waiting for me, it was a good day, but with her, there was always something.

Zach greeted me as I unlock the door. She was on the couch always writing in that damn journal of hers. She had stayed home from the morning sickness. We only spoke with our eyes, making quick contact before I headed to the kitchen and cracked open my bottle. I poured back to back shots to speed things up. If I was going to hear her bitch, I might as well be piss drunk so I don't remember. The last time I blacked out, I woke up to her scrubbing the walls. Some shit about me pissing on the walls again during the middle of the night or the vomit on the bathroom floor or the door I smashed with my fist in a drunken rage. I honestly didn't care.

After I was done with my bottle, I stumbled to the garage to smoke a few bowls. I reviewed my notes from practice and then watched footage of our duals. I didn't feel like hearing her shit, so I played video games until she fell asleep. I would sleep in the other room waiting until my alarm went off, dressing in the same khaki pants and the same red polo shirt that I didn't even bother to wash during the week. I didn't see the problem with drinking if I was able to function at work the next day. Why can't a man have a drink in his own house in peace for crying out loud? Was that too much to ask? She knew not to bring it up or else I'd remind her of the times she was face down in her own puke. My family drank; her family drank. It wasn't a big deal.

Before I left for work, I tossed the pile of bottles and cans in the bin outside. I stashed my weed in my jacket so I could smoke out with a few of the other security guards during our lunch break. This was my fucked up routine over and over again. Repeat the next day with another bottle this time and every time after until I no longer felt the pain.

CHAPTER EIGHTEEN

MISCARRIAGE

I showed him the positive strips. I went to Rite Aid earlier in the week when I missed my period. My breasts were already feeling tender, and I waited for him to leave work before I could vomit. I played the scenario repeatedly in my head, the way I would break the news. No matter what I came up with, nothing seemed right. When would I tell him? How? His reaction would scare me the most, and it was exactly how I anticipated.

"No! I can't have a child right now! How did this happen? You're on birth control!" he shouted.

"I forgot to take it for a few weeks. Things were busy and stressful. I just forgot." I handed him my pregnancy tests with the plus signs, "I even took two just in case." He shook his head, "This is so irritating. I don't need this right now. I can't afford to have a baby," he yelled walking away.

That night, he slept in the spare bedroom, and I slept with Zach on our bed. It was muggy inside the room, so I cracked the window to let the spring breeze grace my body for comfort. I sank quietly into the good night, blaming myself for not remembering something so simple. I pondered what might become of our child. Maybe a basketball player like her momma or a wrestler like his papa. I planned to have a baby shower at Aunt Virgie's house. I pictured my round belly and me cradling my stomach. I would begin to buy maternity clothes and look into daycare options. I drove around my neighborhood the following day and enquired about prices. When he came home, he asked, "How are you feeling?" and I merely replied, "Fine." I didn't know how else to answer such a tough question. He knew I wasn't myself, but he just let it be and didn't bother to ask any more questions the rest of the evening.

I was praying for a girl, a mini-me I could mold into greatness. A girl that would love me unconditionally. I would teach her how to read, write, shoot a J with an ankle breaking crossover. Then, as she attended her first dance, we would shop together and get our hair and nails done, like girls. I tried to stay positive and hoped that he, at some point, would be happy.

But that happiness never came.

I called my gynecologist to set up an appointment for the first trimester. I hid the pregnancy from most people, only telling a few close girlfriends, and I decided I would inform Aunt Virgie after my first trimester visit. But when I called her, I had different news.

When I went to the bathroom in the morning, my underwear was slightly bloody. I read that women, even if pregnant, would experience spots of bleeding during the first trimester. I felt fine, no headache or cramping, and I went to work.

I called him before I left the house, "So is it a miscarriage or not?"

"I don't know. I never miscarried before." My doctor's appointment was in a few days, and during those days, I continued to research miscarriages, but it was still difficult to place. I went about my everyday activity as if nothing bothered me. On the day of my doctor's visit, my gynecologist made me undress spreading my legs wide open as she inserted a cold rod up my uterus. I flinched as it stung from my vagina up to the core of my stomach.

"It could be a miscarriage, but it's hard to tell. There's a fetus in you, but it's not developed to where it should be if you are ten weeks pregnant. If it is a miscarriage, you need to go to the ER immediately. My guess is you are."

It took the next day for the pain to finally hit me. He was in the kitchen cooking dinner, and I was in bed resting, until I let out a violent scream, startling myself. I clutched my stomach, but the pain continued to peak the more I yelled. I struggled to get up, becoming unbalanced and dizzy falling back on the bed.

"The pain will go away. I don't think I need to drive you to the hospital right now." I moved to the couch, so he could go to bed. I turned on the T.V. to find ways to distract my mind from the pain, but nothing worked. Three hours later, he stormed out of the room, "Fine, I'll take you now, I guess."

I screamed the entire ride to the hospital, and the more I screamed, the faster he drove. I reached for his hand to squeeze, but he quickly moved it, "I can't hold your hand and drive at the same time." As we pulled up, he ordered, "Get out, and I'll go park the car." I felt like a toddler taking her first steps as I stumbled through the front door. My throat dry as I explained my miscarriage to the desk clerk. "Have a seat, and we'll call you when it's your turn." Two hours later, a nurse helped me in a wheelchair and pushed me to a room with beeping machines. She transferred me to a bed, and he sat next to me with his hood over his head and his arms crossed. Another cold rod was pushed up my bloody vagina, as I held my breath. "Yes, it's a miscarriage," the doctors confirmed, "sometimes these things never get an explanation. It's just one of those things that happened. Your visit today is $100. Let's get you out of here fast, so you can head home."

We arrived at home just in time for him to go to work. I begged him to stay, but as he shut the door, he said, "I have to go to work." The pain medication wore off in a few hours. My mouth contracted more, and I kept losing massive amounts of blood. Going to the bathroom seemed like the most difficult task. I held myself up against the wall to keep from collapsing clenching my teeth as the pain grew intensely. When I finally made my way to the bathroom, clogs of tissue dispensed from my vagina. My face was grey, and my eyes drenched and puffy. I sat on the toilet to disperse more bloody chunks. I flushed the wet plasma down the toilet when I felt done, but my miscarriage lasted fifteen days. As I made my way back to the couch, Zach sat by my head, tenderly licking my face.

A woman doesn't always have control of her body. My daughter broke into pieces inside me. The life I could create no longer a possibility but now a myth. The world around me was empty, and I would never be able to say with pride, "She's my firstborn."

CHAPTER NINETEEN
BROWN BAG

After getting off work from teaching, I made a stop at Uncle Chunky's house, thirty minutes max, just to check in on him. Things never go as planned when spending time with my uncle and eight hours later, I continued to find myself in his company.

I rode with Uncle Chunky to San Diego City College to pick up a check from a gig he performed earlier in the week. A guy, who introduced himself as Caballo, handed him a check in the parking lot. On the drive back to Uncle Chunky's house, we stopped by Ken's liquor store. Uncle Chunky handed me a list of things to buy while he waited in Black Beauty, his 1980 Chevy truck. List: bread, margarine, blue dressing, and a box of instant mash potatoes. Verbally a bottle of brandy, paying for the bottle with the few bucks he won on a scratcher. "Tell Ken thanks for cashing in the check. He'll know what I mean." I nodded and went inside for the scavenger hunt. After collecting the items, a homeless man pranced through the entrance of the liquor store. He beamed at my feet, "Those are some nice shoes." I thanked him, gazing at his missing a leg. The missing leg was wrapped in a towel, an upside-down orange construction cone tied with a bungee cord holding his leg for balance. When I went back to my uncle's truck, I shared with him the exchange I had with the homeless man.

Uncle Chunky let out his signature raspy laugh, "It's the little things we need to appreciate," he said as he turned on the ignition, and we cruised towards Radio Drive.

When we arrived, Uncle Chunky marched straight to the kitchen to cook dinner, a turkey meatloaf decorated with mini carrots, green onions, peppers, a side of instant mashed potatoes, and toast based with margarine. "Make that sucker look cosmetically good so people want to eat it." The juice flowed like a river of minerals as Uncle Chunky removed the meatloaf from the oven, "Here you go, Veer. Lick your chops."

As I began digging into my plate, the witch stormed in the kitchen, throwing the plate food in my uncle's face, "I don't eat meat," the meatloaf shattered into pieces as it hit the ground, the juice staining my uncle's shirt. He quickly apologized placing the fallen pieces back on the tray as she stood over him clutching her teeth. Her black wig squeezed on her head like if someone was squeezing a lime into a shot of tequila. "Why is she always here?" She demanded, foaming at the mouth. "She's leaving right now. She helped me pick up the check from the gig," Uncle Chunky pulled out his wallet and shivered, handing her a few twenties to weather the storm. "She needs to leave now, Chunky," she yelled snatching the money and slamming the door to her cave.

"Thanks for dinner, Chunk. I should head home now."

"Take a ride with the Chunkster," he begged with the circumstances of his eyes.

We cruised Encanto at 10 mph, cars passing us along the road, stopping at a few of his homies' houses as they came outside to chop it up with him. Driving up and down the same roads, he received a call, "It's my old lady." She ordered my uncle to drive through KFC.

"I thought she didn't eat meat. She can feed herself. Plus, it's 10:00 p.m."

"She wants mac and cheese, a Sprite, and baked beans." On our way back, my uncle made another stop at a liquor store to buy more alcohol, a pack of smokes, and another scratcher, "For the road."

We drove up to his house again, "Go hand this to my old lady. Do it for Big Daddy, and don't say anything." The house was lonely and stunk of burnt sage. I left the bag on the dining table and returned outside to my uncle's truck. He parked on the side, blowing smoke out the window. "My mom use to put our lunches in brown bags, like these," Uncle Chunky remembered as he took out his brandy and emptied the bottle in one swig. He placed the bottle under his bench seat. "The bag had to last all week. The other kids laughed at me. They had Lone Star or Mickey Mouse lunch pails that were polished. Theirs came with a thermos filled with milk and a peanut butter and jelly sandwich. Mine came with two burritos, one bean and one meat wrapped in foil. An occasional Twinkie. Once I was done with my lunch, I had to save the bag and place it in my back pocket. It had to last the whole week." Uncle Chunky neatly folded the brown bag, stretching the creases for a sharper edge. "My dad was the only one who had a real lunchbox, a heavy industrial box made for the work of a farmer. My mom cooked him four burritos, sliced an apple or an orange, and water. For dessert, two slices of bread with strawberry jelly in the middle." Uncle Chunky lit another cigarette, "The kids at school looked at me funny while I ate. I was ashamed, so I hid behind the classroom building and gobbled my food. By the end of the week, the brown bag was covered in grease, torn at the bottom, wrinkled from the top, so I appreciate it every time I had a new brown bag, a treasure. A tired brown bag like me. But like me, one day will be appreciated."

CHAPTER TWENTY

NANCY

Aunt Virgie called to inform me that Uncle Chunky was back at Paradise Valley Hospital, also known as Death Valley Hospital for its highest death rates in the county. He was admitted for pneumonia, but the doctors found complications in his blood and lungs, which could stem from the smoking, drinking, eating, lack of exercise, or all of the above.

My students designed a get well card decorated with hearts and balloons. A student, Eddie, developed an interest in my uncle since I shared stories in class. Eddie wrote a fantasy story where my uncle played at a halftime show during a Charger-Raider game. The Beatles performed including John and George. They rose from their graves to play, and Eddie went on stage to breakdance to the music. When my uncle and the Beatles were done playing, John and George returned to their graves, disappearing into the ground. My uncle read the card and smiled, "Eddie boy," he shouted in the air as he finished reading Eddie's story, "put it on the wall, Veer." I tacked the card next to a picture of my uncle performing at a Cinco de Mayo show.

The visit with my uncle was short, since the witch was glued to his hip complaining about the fans at football games, "Nothing but a bunch of drunks." This was an indirect comment towards my student's story. My uncle and I looked at each other, and I rolled my eyes. "I should be leaving." I gave my uncle our signature high-five, patted his stomach, and exited his room quicker than I entered.

As I was leaving the hospital, I approached the sliding doors of the main entrance. In the patio area, a lady in a wheelchair searched the ground. She must have spotted me at the corner of her eyes, "Darling," she pointed, "that red shiny thing." I squinted, a wire hid between fallen leaves.

"This?" I picked it up and handed it to her.

"Yes, thanks, sweetie," she grabbed the wire and headed outside. There were two more red wires by the exit. I walked after her and handed her the others I found.

"Are those for me? Groovy. I have something for you but don't think anything about it." She unzipped a leather toiletry bag and took out one Hershey's Kiss, "For you." Her red hair sagged to the side of her face, and her glasses somewhat covered her gray eyes. Her left hand was missing three fingers and when she smiled, an inch gap appeared between her canine and front teeth.

"How long have you been in here?"

"Since Wednesday."

"That's when my uncle was admitted. He's in room 651."

"He's right next door. I'm in 654. I knock on the wall, and he'll hear me."

"They might let him go on Sunday. What about you?"

She bowed her head, placing her glasses on her head, and wiped her eyes, "Who can tell? They may have to cut off more," she sliced her hand across her knee. She lifted her gown to show the infection spreading, her skin tucked into her knees, "This medicine makes me itch. At first, they gave me Vicodin. I should have kept my big mouth shut. The only thing left on me is my nose." She reached back into her bag and pulled out a pack of cigarettes, "The nurses gave me a timed break. Last time, they sent security to find me. Just for that, I'll have two cigarettes." She pulled out a lighter lighting the tip. No problem for a lady with three missing fingers.

"So what are you making?"

"I don't know. I collect random things, different flowers, marbles, and pennies I find on the floor. I can't miss them. I have the advantage of seeing things down here. I gather leaves and put them in a vase. It's not worth any value, but nobody in the world has anything like it." She paused to take a puff, "I have a jar full of rooster feathers. I'm making dream catchers for family and friends, though I don't have many. Karen lives in Las Vegas. Danny's in jail serving his last year. He saw pictures. Nathaniel's in Sacramento," she wiped her eyes again, "I don't want to be a burden to them. The chair weighs 300 pounds. Then, picking me up and putting me in the car," she shook her head as if she did something wrong.

"I didn't catch your name?"

"Nancy."

"I'm Vera."

"There's nothing worse then meeting a stranger who whines and complains about life, but I consider myself blessed. When I go back to my room, I'm going to pray to God and maybe cry a little. I don't know how you feel about God, but I think things, situations, happen for a reason." Nancy took her good arm and pointed it to her left. She flicked her cigarette on the ground and lit another, "You know I usually don't do that."

"What kind of music do you like?"

"Oh, Luther Vandross, Kenny G, anything really, reggae." Nancy smiled, dancing in her seat, snapping her fingers.

"My uncles play in a band. They compose all their music. My Uncle Chunky is the lead singer and writes their songs, and Tio Rick plays all the instruments. They are called Los Alacranes, The Scorpions in English."

"*Cantan la musica en Español?*" Nancy said in her broken Spanish.

"They sing both English and Spanish."

"Groovy, music is a beautiful thing, man," Nancy closed her eyes and deeply inhaled, "when you don't have anybody music is the only thing that will speak to you."

"That's a beautiful necklace you have."

It was a dreamcatcher made of black marble with red and lime stones, "My friend gave it to me. We met at church, but I stopped going, and so did she. I found her later. God wanted me to hook up with her again." Nancy bounced in her wheelchair, saluting the sky with another cigarette in her hand, "God. We used to play poker, watch movies, eat popcorn, but I refused a lot. It is difficult going to the bathroom because my chair is too wide. She says her husband can pick me up in his truck. Still, I don't want to feel helpless. Do you sing with your uncles?"

"No, I'm a dancer."

"Groovy, what kind of dance?"

"Folklorico."

"Never heard of it. Oh wait, is that the one with the beautiful dresses?"

"Correct."

"Right on. There's that park, Chicano Park. That place is beautiful."

"I've performed there since I was three. My uncles play during the park's anniversary, too."

Nancy threw her last cigarette on the pavement, "Right on. I'm going to head back to my room," she drove past me, the automatic doors opened, and she turned to me, "what's your name again, dear?"

"Vera."

"Vera," she repeated and headed down the hallway. I shook in the cold while Nancy's cigarette burned at my feet. I began walking to my car and took a look back. By now, Nancy reached the end of the hallway. I couldn't explain it, but I knew she was special the moment I saw her. As I gazed down the empty hallway, I knew Nancy felt she wasn't worth much value, but someday I hoped she realized she was unique because there was nobody else in the world like her.

CHAPTER TWENTY-ONE

JUNIOR

I was on my way Downtown to listen to live music, dressed up, meeting nobody. A night to myself would do me some good to get away from home. I took my journal with me and decided I would write about all the happy couples as I slouched at the bar to avoid in any small talk with drunken strangers.

Before making my way on the freeway, I pulled into a gas station across the street from the old Fam Bam, a spot where the homies stole their back to school gear. As I stepped out of my truck, an elderly dark-skinned man scrubbed car windows with a used napkin. When he was done, he waved through the window, but the cars sped off, rushing to their destination. I observed him while pumping my gas until he approached me. Curious, I asked his name. In a slurred speech he replied, "Junior," fumbling between each letter.

"Are you hungry, Junior?"

"Yaah, ma'am." I reached for my wallet and pulled out a twenty dollar bill placing it in his palm without regret. Knowing me, the money would be spent on a few bottles of beer anyways. Junior shifted, gazing at his hand, and he smiled with his eyes. "Thhaank yoouu, maami." Junior wore a torn windbreaker and a beat up cap, his gray hairs poking out from the sides.

"Do you want a hug?" I reached for him leaning my head against his arm, accidentally planting my red lipstick on his sleeve. He pointed at the mark in laughter. "Get something good to eat and drink for tonight." I hopped back in my truck as we waved goodbye. Junior bounced from car to car with his crumpled napkin knocking at windows. I adjusted my mirror, and as I drove off, I continued driving down the road until Junior disappeared.

I wrote about my brief encounter with Junior when I arrived at the bar. I thought about the cold night and if he found shelter. I felt connected to Junior because he wandered in thin air, searching to survive in a cruel world with such a merciful soul. His hug was genuine, one I couldn't find at home. Same with Nancy. Two strangers that made me feel loved, even if it was for a brief moment. I hoped they felt the love in return.

CHAPTER TWENTY-TWO

SANDRITA

I grew up watching Sandrita handle her business with the men. I jotted down notes in my journal, and one day I would apply her techniques to have some fun if I even had the balls to leave. It was never a dull moment when Sandrita was behind the counter at Chiquita's. A line formed out the door as the men rushed from work, running red lights, and weaving in and out of traffic just for a glimpse of the natural triple D cups. She had *tetas* that looked like they belonged on an Aztec statue, simply perfect. When the men drooled, she'd pat their *babas* with a napkin, like a mother would for her newborn baby. The accessories in her bag were a glitter wallet with a stack of 1's; a matching glitter makeup bag; an eyelash curler; a brush kit; a comb; a pack of peppermint gum; a book; and a blunt. "I use everything in here," Sandrita said as she applied her makeup during her shifts.

Her talents were her body parts and also the most fun. If a man asked for a cherry, she sucked on it and then slid it down his throat with her tongue, leaving the imprint of her glossy pink lipstick, her signature mark. Her regulars bought her flowers and stuffed animals, in which Sandrita showed her appreciation by humping the stuffed animals. When the music played, Sandrita stopped pouring shots and danced on the countertop, lifting her skirt, while the crowd whistled,

"Shake it, baby." All men where at her discretion, and she'd pick, "Eeny-meeny-miny-moe," arranging her men by nickname in her phone, the first contact, Asshole. Her boy toys came in all shapes and forms: blue collar to lawyers to cholos, married to divorce, boys barely old enough to buy their first beer to great-grandfathers hanging by their last thread, but one visit to Sandrita added another ten years to any man's life.

And Sandrita never backed down from any jealous bitch. "What's this bitch's problem? Does she know I'll fuck her up?" As a teenager, she fought the other girls in the school bathrooms, the ones that spread rumors running their mouths. She didn't give a fuck, fighting bitches in mini skirts and high heels, grabbing them by the *greñas*, bras flying off, chi-chis flapping in the air. She may have lost her clothes in the process, but she never took an L.

When the men proposed, Sandrita had the same response, "I've never felt that dumb. I wasn't born on the ranch. I'm from SD. I'm not going to change for no man. I'm not even trip'n. If a guy tells me to get off my high horse, I tell him fuck no. I worked too fucking hard to stay on this damn horse." The manager would have to exchange the cash drawer when it overflowed every couple of hours. She could down tequila harder than any dude at the bar, which made the men love her even more. Sandrita ran the show. Everyone knew it, and nobody got in her way.

CHAPTER
TWENTY-THREE

ROOM 443

Chunky laid in the hospital bed compressed in a blanket. He looked at his brothers with confusion when they entered, Rick wore in his usual cut off sleeve shirt and basketball shorts, and Ralph dressed in his homeless clothes. As they entered the room, they took a spot on each side of Chunky's bed. They were the first visitors of the day to spread their brotherly love.

"Your kidney and your liver are malfunctioning. Your kidney takes care of the piss and the shit, and it's not functioning due to all the booze you've been drinking all your life." Ralph said as he leaned forward to snap a picture of Chunky, who gave him a baffled look.

"We drink just as much as him, so don't blame it on that," Rick countered as he crossed his arms in a defensive mood.

"Well, I know, but we don't live his chaotic life."

"We have a gig today, right?" Chunky, weary from the medications, slowly turned his eyes to Rick.

"No, it was yesterday at the Jacob Center, the Columbus gig."

"Oh boy, oh boy. I missed the gig?" Chunky let out an ugly cough. He tapped his chest a few times and gagged some more, "I missed the gig?" he asked in uncertainty.

The door swung opened, and the brothers shifted their attention to the front of the room, where a young man dressed in burgundy scrubs with slick black hair entered, "How are you doing, folks? How's he doing, better?"

"Pretty good because his wife hasn't arrived yet."

"Well, she called. She's going to come."

"Can you please let me know when she's here, so we can leave?"

"It will be like in an hour, Ralph. We'll be gone by then."

"And you are?"

"I'm the nurse. My name is Christian," he answered flashing his name badge.

"Thank you for everything that you do for my brother," Rick extended his arm to shake Christian's hand.

"Can you go stay with him at his house?"

"No, I can't do that."

"We just want to make sure he has the proper care over there. It's pretty chaotic at his house. I ain't the one to gossip, so you didn't hear it from me," Ralph laughed adjusting his glasses and flaunting his missing teeth.

"Ralph, *cállate*," Rick mumbled under his lips for his brother to shut up.

"How did you sleep last night, Mr. Sánchez?"

"With my eyes closed."

"I'm going to give him his medication soon. It's going to make him poop. It's just a heads up."

"Is he taking it verbal or is he shooting it up?"

"Through his mouth. Did you eat breakfast?"

Chunky speculated the question, "No. How do you bring the bed up?" Christian reached for the remote that was by Chunky's side.

"Is your food better here than at Kaiser? Kaiser has good food. The last time I had pneumonia I was there for four days. I loved it. I didn't want to leave."

"Sharp's the best hospital, Ralph."

"I don't know about that. They gave me the royal treatment at Kaiser."

With his hagged eyes retreating into his sockets, Chunky repeated in short breaths, "I missed the gig?"

"It's alright. It's not the first time. We did a good job."

"I want to get an Alacran picture," Ralph interrupted.

"Don't put this on Facebook."

"I don't know how to do Facebook."

"You send it to the cousins in Blythe, and they blast it. This is not a Facebook moment."

"The hell it isn't," Ralph ignored his younger brother's request and snagged a quick photo of Chunky.

"Okay. When you're croaking, we're going to take pictures of you."

"They aren't doing a documentary on my life. I'm not worth shit. He is," Ralph pointed to Chunky taking another picture. This time, Chunky grinned a little.

"Okay, so is this the end of the documentary? Is this the last episode?"

"I'm just saying if Mark Day can film my brother taking a shit, I can film him in a hospital bed. I just thought it would be nice to have an Alacran picture."

"You take lousy pictures. I delete all of them. You can't make them out. This needs to come up more." Rick stood from his chair, adjusting the headboard once again.

"Then why are you worried about me plastering it on Facebook?"

"Well, if I was in his condition, I wouldn't want my picture taken." Chunky shifted his head from side to side as his brothers argued over social media, which neither one of them knew how to operate.

"Well, he's not saying no, and he's the biggest ham in the world, okay."

"Speaking of ham, is there any ham here? What's this, coffee?" Rick picked up the mug that was on the portable table and gave it a sniff, "Do you want some mud? You have creamer here and sugar. Want me to fix it for you?"

"They never give me anything here."

"Rick, I've never seen you in such a humanitarian mood. You're full of shit. I'm the older brother here. When he dies, I'm in charge."

"They never give me anything," Chunky groaned again trying to grab their attention. That didn't seem to work.

"Virgie is ultimately in charge right now," Rick bickered as he scanned through Chunky's leftovers with a fork.

"They never give me anything," Chunky repeated louder.

"Well, she's not here right now."

"They never give me anything." The fourth times was the charm.

"Do you want some jelly in your oatmeal?" Rick untwisted a strawberry jar that was next to the coffee, "Ummmm, I'll sweeten it up."

"You guys are going to fucking poison me," Chunky began his wisecracks as he rubbed his eyes.

"You're already poisoned."

"Oh, look the sun is shining," Chunky's eyes brighten, and he smiled towards the light shining through his room.

"Yes, place in the sun. We dedicated that song to you last night. They're coming in here to give him his meds now. Let's go."

"Are there any clogs?"

"Who's that?"

"The nurses." Rick waddled out the room.

"Don't leave, Rick."

"We'll be right back once they're done giving you the meds so you can *cacar*."

"Are you done shitting?" Rick asked as he and Ralph returned to the room. Ralph approached Chunky again and pointed the antenna of the flip phone into his chest.

"Hey, you know what? You should do an absentee ballot."

"A what?"

"An absentee ballot. I can go to the county and get you an absentee ballot so you can vote for Obama before November 4th. You're not going to make it for the election. Are you?"

"I don't know. Ask God up there," Rick plopped down gesturing to the ceiling, "don't ask Dr. Frankenstein. Chunk will be here November 4th. What's today? The 14th."

"Your face doesn't look good, Ray."

"Yeah it does. I mean if you're in the hospital, are you going to look like Jack LaLanne?"

"Who are those kids in the fairy tales that had red cheeks with freckles? Hansel and Gretel, right? The ones that drink the gingerbread."

"Don't tell him his face looks like that," Rick poured Chunky a glass of orange juice handing it to him, "here, pretend there's vodka in there." Once he's done chugging the juice in two long swallows, Chunky creased his chin and lifted his arm in the air for a Chicano power salute, his medical bracelets stuck to his wrist.

"What's up with morning football, Ray?"

"Can they put that monitor up any higher, shit? What are you like Lew Alcindor?" Rick studied the remote trying to find the on button. Rick could play any instrument invented by man, but he didn't know how to operate basic accessories.

"I thought you loved football?"

"I do."

"What is your message to *Aztlán* as we speak? Mark Day wants to know what's going on with you."

"Who?"

"Mark Day. If you need a priest on sight, he knows a couple of good ones." Mark Day was also a former priest who gave Cesar Chavez communion when he fasted and has been working on a documentary on Chunky for the last ten years.

"Well, he ain't dying yet, Ralph. He doesn't need his last rights read," Rick countered pressing multiple buttons, none which turned on the television.

"I can't believe that… umm… I can't believe—"

"That the Chargers won."

"No…that…umm—"

Interrupting Chunky's deep train of thought, Ralph scrutinized his brother's hospital visits, "You already made a complete circle, Ray. I don't know what you're waiting for."

"It's not his time, Ralph. He just wants you to croak."

"Paradise, Reba, Grossmont, Mission Hills, La Mesa, Lemon Grove, back to Grossmont. *Eres sangrado*. You're full of blood." Ralph made his point by drawing circles in the air with his left finger as his glasses slid down his flat nose.

"That's okay. This is the best hospital."

"That's cuz the people they keep here are gross."

"Is that the way I look?" Chunky appeared confused by his brother's diagnoses.

"You should see the shit that's coming out of you. That's gross, too."

"Then, don't look at it."

"Rick, I'm not here to fight with you, okay. If you're going to fight with anybody, do it with Betty. I ain't here to live'n my brother's life up," Ralph switched to his off key singing voice, "because *no puedo vivir mas sin ti. No puedo vivir mas si ti, mi amor. I can't live without you. I can't live anymore without you, my love. La la la la la.* Back me up," Ralph waved his hands in the air like if he was directing an orchestra.

"I'll buy you a pint of Potters if you shave that nasty beard. You look like that guy King Edward."

Chunky turned to Ralph and chuckled before catching his breath, "What happened to me last night, Rick?"

"Betty called me."

"She was screaming and yelling."

"Not really."

"Just lie. Just lie to him," Ralph winked to Rick from across the room, "she was screaming and yelling."

"You forgot about the gig, and how you're not going to make it."

"How did she know?"

"I guess you passed out in her hands. Your kids said that night and that morning you where acting weird."

"And they haven't mentioned forty years of Betty acting weird? Please. May a lighting bolt strike me if I'm not telling the truth."

"Don't say that," Chunky begged since he was strapped to his bed as if he was in a straitjacket, like Hannibal Lector.

"Rick, I got a picture of you playing yesterday. He's now the only *gordo* of Los Alacranes. Right?"

"I don't know."

"Well take a look to your right. You're not blind yet, are you?"

"Ralph, shut up."

"Are you Oliver Hardy?" Chunky clowned referencing to the early comedy classic.

"All he needs is one of those little hats. By the way, Luis Natividad told everyone you were in the hospital over the microphone, and you guys are worried about this shit," Ralph shoved his flip phone in Chunk's face, "at least I can speak. He's my brother, and pretty soon, I'll be the commander of the family. When he croaks, I'm next to the throne."

"Virgie's the commander."

"She'll be the queen, and I'll be the king. I'll be the commander of the Sánchez family. I command, and I demand. I'll rule with an iron hand."

"How does this shit work?" Rick said finally turning on the television, "Where's sports?"

"Fuck. My dick hurts, man."

"Why? Did you pull an all-nighter?"

"They put that thing in there."

"Catheter."

"Yeah, that mother fucker hurts like a mother fucker."

"What does? What did they do to you?" Ralph looked up from the pictures on his phone.

"His catheter."

"What does that mean?"

"They put it inside your penis hole."

Ralph screamed, "Awwweee!"

"I don't know how to work this fucking thing," Rick said as he grew frustrated navigating for a game.

"Jive suckers."

"You can't have *chorizo* anymore?"

"I'm not a thousand huevos away," Ralph sang a verse from Chunky's infamous song, *Chorizo Sandwich,* a humorous love ballad about a cheating *vieja,* "remember when OLE said you had no *huevos* on your wedding day?"

"Can you have banana bread?"

"Yeah. Where we at?"

"Grossmont Hospital."

"Is there banana bread here?"

"Why don't we ask first. I just want to make sure you can have it."

"He's been having banana nut bread at every damn hospital, so what's the difference?"

"Do you remember coming over here in the ambulance last night? They had to 911 you."

"Ray, you're just pushing the envelope left and right. You know that."

"I'm pushing what?"

"You're pushing the envelope."

"Waahh. Waahh. Waahh," Chunky blazed his eyes at the wall.

"He seems pretty normal to me. You look good, man."

"Oh yeah, he looks real good. He's lying in a hospital bed. How great can he look?"

"Ralph, he needs all the positive strokes he can get."

"I'm not here to give him positive strokes. I'm giving him reality," Ralph not done with his live concert, *"I'm looking for a real reality because it's about me and you. Da da da da da da.* You should have a reality show, Ray. You and your wife. Then, they'll put hidden cameras in your house. People will tune into it every day. It would be a big hit. You guys have to find a way to make money for all your hospital bills. Stop begging for money with your fundraisers. You have one like every month."

"Where's my bread?"

"Here comes the nurse. Is it okay if he has banana nut bread?"

"Are you allergic to nuts?" Christian, returning to the room, asked in his polite demeanor.

"Sometimes."

"He has no nuts. He said you guys took them away when you guys stuck that thing up his penis, and he doesn't like it."

"You did that to me, huh?"

"That wasn't me. That was down in ER."

"Why did you do that?"

"I didn't do that. Hey Ricardo," Christian called into the monitor, "can you warm up the coffee and bring it to room 443?"

"Where can we purchase the bread?"

"He actually can't have any. Right now they have him on a strict diet."

"That's what got you into this mess in the first place."

"No, it's not, Ralph."

"Eating greasy Mexican food all your life."

"Awwee man," and when Chunky muttered those words, the hospital phone rang startling him.

"Don't answer it. It might be his wife. Have you met his wife?" Ralph asked Christian, who was writing notes on the whiteboard.

"I met her yesterday."

"Yuck! We'll be leaving when she gets here. Trust me. We're the brothers. We can't stand her fucking guts. We'll be leaving by 11:00 a.m. She's not a morning person."

In slow motion, Chunky picked up the phone, "Hello. Who's this? They stuck that damn thing in my penis. Ralph and Rick. Should they go? Can they stay? They can stay, please."

"I'm going to grab his medications. I have to call the doctor and update him right now because this is new," Christian tapped the urine bag that dangled at the edge of the bed with his foot, "that's blood."

"We're getting ran out, Ralph. Via phone." Ralph stretched his back like a pissed off cat, and flipped off the phone with both his hands, sticking out his tongue. The nurse placed his hands inside his pocket and left the room.

"They say I can't have banana bread. Alright, bye," Chunky handed the receiver to Rick, who hung it up, "where's my bread banana nut?" Chunky questioned reversing the order of the words.

"You can't have any. You're on a strict diet."

"It's not going to kill me."

"Your wife is taking care of that." Ralph said with a straight face, and Chunky's laugh echoed in the room as Ralph caught the moment with his flip phone.

"It seems like you're drunk," Rick joked, which Chunky laughed even more, "are you taking shots of brandy? You have your eyes like a *pinche borracho.* You know what Luis Natividad said, 'hey don't tell anyone this is a Christopher Columbus gig.' *Viva La Raza*! Shit if everyone would've known. Fucking scabs Los Alacranes. We played for Christopher *Colon* yesterday. He discovered America. Ooohh, don't let the Enriquezes and your wife know. Here comes the other nurse."

There was a knock, "Hello, hello. Good morning. How are you? Did you order the coffee?" The nurse said with his Spanish accent.

"Hey what kind of coffee is that?" Chunky enquired.

"Regular, I think. *Tu hablas Español?* Me, too."

"*Boricua. Puerto Rico libre*," Ralph said assuming the nurse was from the tropical island.

"*Soy Colombiano*," the nurse corrected.

"*Tengo una pregunta*," there was a short pause as Chunky thought about his question, "*no recuerdo.*"

"He doesn't remember. Is it about the coffee?"

"Ah," Chunky raised his hand in the air like a school kid asking a question, "*ese madre que me meterón en el cochi.* That mother that you stuck in my nasty."

"*¿La medecina?*"

"*No era medecina.*"

"He's asking about the catheter."

"*¿Todavía está dentro en mí?* Is it still in me?"

Ralph screamed as he covered his crotch dropping his phone.

"It's for when you pee, when you *miar*. It has to stay in you."

"*Chingada madre.*"

"Ralph!"

"I share his pain, okay. How would you like to have that shit up your penis?"

"He has no choice. It's either that or he pisses all over himself."

"Well, I piss in my pants all the time. Just wipe it off."

"Are you ready to leave?"

"Why? Don't leave me, Rick."

"I've given you my word to death do us part. I'm sticking by you. *I'm sticking to my guy like the bird to the feather. I'm telling you from the start I can't be torn apart from my guy. As a matter of opinion I think he's tops.*"

"Enough, Ralph!"

With each beat, Ralph pounded on Chunky's chest like a television that didn't work, "*My opinion is he's the king of the crop.*"

"Don't slap me."

"*No handsome face can ever take the place of my guy.*"

"You just said his face looked shitty."

"*He may not be a movie star, but when it comes to being happy, we are. No one can take me away from my guy.*" Ralph patted Chunky and planted a kiss on his head.

"Do you have security here?" Rick asked the nurse who was patiently waiting with the coffee.

"*¿Quieres el café?*" The nurse handed the coffee mug to Ralph, who stopped singing.

"It's hot."

"That's why it's got a handle on it."

"*¿Qué es tu nombre?*"

"Ricardo." He removed the cup from Ralph and handed the coffee to Chunky, who reached for the handle.

"*Tocayo,*" Ralph pointed to Rick who shared the same name as the nurse, "but he was born *en la cuna de Aztlán.*"

"*¿Qué parte de Colombia?*"

"*Bogotá.*"

"That's the capital."

"The ladies there are beautiful because they always get runner-up in the Ms. Universe pageant."

"That's where the *cumbia* originated."

"And the chi-chi Zumba," Ricardo removed the cover to a straw for Chunky's coffee, "are you going to stick that in his penis again?"

"*Me duele ese madre.* That mother hurts. I want it out of me."

"Can you get up by yourself?"

"That's why you're here. You can't get up by yourself. That's why you piss and shit in tubes."

"You can't function, Ray," Ralph jumped in the air with animation, "I know what you need. You need Sandrita here." Chunky's eyes lit up like a Christmas tree, "We'll bring her again."

"I'll be back with his lunch in twenty minutes."

"*Almuerzo* is lunch, right? I thought that was breakfast."

"*Desayudo* is breakfast," Ralph corrected.

"I thought lunch was *lonche*."

"That's cuz you're a *pocho*, Rick. We're all *pochos*. Hey, us *pochos* got to stick together. Ray, you're the grand *pocho*."

"I'm a Spaniard," Chunky sipped his coffee with care, the steam mingling in the air.

"He is going nuts."

"We all are in a way. Sánchez. It didn't come over from Iraq or Saudi Arabia."

"You're right, Rick. It's about time you accepted your Spanish roots."

"Well, weren't you rooting for Spain during the World Cup?"

"Yeah, cuz they were playing England. Ray, you and Betty have pushed that Indian shit for too long. It's spooky."

"Let's leave. They have to put the bag under his ass now."

"I didn't ask for it."

"Well, here it comes. Let's go."

"Rick, you're acting like an Indian."

"No, I'm not. I'm a Spaniard. Ralph, we've been here an hour and a half."

"He doesn't want us to leave," Ralph leaned his egg head with Chunky's Humpty Dumpty head, and they both smiled at Rick.

"Hey, I miss the gig? How did that happen?"

"Your wife tripped you. Ray, you're my favorite brother."

"I got to go. *Ya cumpli.*" Fulfilled with the visit, Rick and Ralph made their escape, "We'll be back tomorrow morning."

As the door closed, Chunky, wrapped in a hospital blanket, whispered with sips of air, "Don't leave me," and he closed his eyes waiting for tomorrow.

CHAPTER TWENTY-FOUR

UNOPENED PRISON LETTER

Dear Veer Beer,

When you're betrayed and hurt by someone you love, trust, and believe in, it's like the worse feeling in the world. Your heart drops. You lose your breath for a quick second. Your eyes get watery, you get chills, and you're in denial for a brief moment. Then, you realize it's all bad and you get to wondering why me, what did I do, and is it my fault. It's never an easy thing to cope with or get over. I'm sorry for you having to go through such drama. It does appear as though that his behavior was extremely selfish, idiotic, inconsiderate, and downright wrong. Cheating is wrong and pretty much the worst thing you can do in a relationship. But there are some occasions where it's needed or where some deserve it. However, I don't feel that in your case it was needed or deserved. To me, it seemed like the opportunity presented itself, and he felt that he could get away with it and "what you don't know won't hurt you."

But sooner or later what you do in the dark always comes to light. Plus, most men tend to think that we can do whatever we want and get away with it anyways whether it be wrong or right. It's like we just know that we are going to be forgiven like we got chances. But some of us fail to realize that what comes around goes around, and it's not so fun when we are the ones getting played. At the same time, not all women are spiteful in that way. However, they still manage to find other ways to get back at us or put it all in our face. It takes time to forgive and forget, but when it comes to this type of situation, you can never forget, but you can forgive. You always find yourself second guessing yourself and your partner for the simple fact that you don't wanna make the same mistakes you made or play the fool again. Which is why I pretty much avoid relationships.

It takes a lot of effort from both sides for it to work out. There's always gonna be drama sooner or later, always going to be temptations and always going to be ups and downs. No relationship is perfect, but yet we strive for perfection in everything we do. What it all comes down to is, is he or she worth all of the bullshit, all the effort, all the drama, all the ups and downs? That is something you must figure out for yourself. Agree with yourself with what you will and will not tolerate, and stick with it. Stand firm for what you believe in cuz you must love yourself completely in order to have a righteous relationship with another person. Otherwise, you are always going to be used and abused or taken advantage of. You must remember that you are grown, so no need to play little kid games or go tit for tat. It's about what's best for you mentally, physically, emotionally, and spiritually. That's for you to decide, not anyone else. You know your worth so never play yourself short or let anyone else make you think differently. I hope you were able to make all your decisions clear minded and to fit your wants and needs. Just be cautious, and learn from your mistakes. Don't let them remain mistakes, turn them into life lessons, and educate yourself as you would in school. Stay on top of things, and don't allow things to get to a point where you're second guessing anything. Do what you feel you need to do in order to obtain your happiness. If you feel you both need counseling, then seek it. If it's more time apart, take it. It's hard and complicated to figure out, but it's necessary. I hope that he can get it together for you and himself. It's a start for him to seek outside advice, and it seems like it's helping. Just try to make sure he keeps it going in case he ever finds himself in another bind. Make sure you two keep clear communication between each other. For that will always help. Remember, instead of settling for less, settle for what's best, babes.

You can always keep holding back with your true feelings and emotions, but eventually, it will come out sooner or later. All it takes is a big fight or perhaps some alcohol. At the same time, why keep torturing yourself and making yourself suffer when he did that to you already. Progress is the best thing after such an incident, and I can understand why you wouldn't want to regress. But some things are better left unsaid than said. However, there are some things that need to be said in order for both sides to truly move forward, progress, and truly forgive. It takes a two-way street, not one. It makes no sense for one of you to move on and forward while the other pretends to, all the while you're hurting inside. Your foundation is bound to crumble if you don't create more solidness. Sometimes, you have to take that gamble and lay all the cards out on the table face up. Certain things can leave to faith to decide. Certain things you can change, but there are occasions where you must take that chance and hope faith prevails. Just believe in it, and keep it.

Well, cuz-n sorry for taking so long to get back. Sometimes the days are really long and tiring. Hope that you're still in good and high spirits when this gets to you. Hope you and him are still doing good and better, so stay up. Hope you have fun at the Charger games you will attend this year. Stay strong, cuz-n. Keep up your faith, keep your head up, and stay pushing forward through the thick and thin. Look forward to your next letter. Love and miss you lots.

Your littlest cuz-n,
Nando

CHAPTER TWENTY-FIVE

NOVEMBER 23RD

Staying with you is like doing time, but it's not jail
This whole relationship has failed.
You were the thorn in my side
Flipped upside down
It killed me inside.

Even your parents admit this was your lowest blow.
Sending pictures of you and her to your boys.
When I received the call, I was informed
I wouldn't see my cousin anymore.

November 23rd Nando was gone
You were at her house ripping off her glittery thong
Lied again, the same old song.
Nasty mind caught every time
It's the same story written over time.

You told your boys to delete the pictures when done,
But you're so fucking dumb.
You didn't take your own advice
When you left the pictures open on my device.

You have a great imagination with such manipulation
Left to interpretation and her stimulation.

Your fingers trickled down her side
Cum inside her or else it's suicide
Begin to swallow your pride to justify
A world renown cheater never satisfied.

You copied what was right
But even God couldn't show you the light
Because you were caught up in your 3D lies.

How does it feel to be the scum of mother earth?
Polluted her even at the time of your precious birth,
Like her, you killed me without a weapon
Only a master of beguilement deception.

Questioning my own existence
It makes sense when you kept me at a distance
Fiddling in my mind with my own resistance.
The hardest time of my life
Putting Nando to rest,
There was emptiness inside my chest
Short of breath
But not short enough to be close to death.

How could you do this to me?
On the day my cousin died, you fucking cheated on me!
It was my fault cuz I just let it be.
Your dick cost me my insanity
From this placed called reality.

Grown but I ran away from home,
So I wrote a simple poem
To keep me alive
One last time
Before I wave to Nando my final goodbye.

CHAPTER TWENTY-SIX

CHOLA

"Are you going to leave him? If you continue to put up with him, I don't want to fucking hear it." We all have that homegirl that keeps it one-hundred all the time. Chola was from Pacoima and was harder than any dude on her block. Even dudes fresh out of the joint didn't touch her or her *tias*. These *rucas* wore Dickies with their lips and eyebrows outlined in black liner. The white wife beaters with a canvas belt. Tattoos on their knuckles with a full can of Aqua Net stuck to their bangs and razors tucked under their tongues. Chola was 4'11, but she stood her ground, so when I was looking for a shoulder to cry on, she wasn't that shoulder. "Stop being such a little bitch. Put on your big girl panties and grow a pair of fucking ovaries," she advised.

You can take Chola out of the barrio, but you can't take the barrio out of Chola. We met when we were students beginning our college journey together at Grossmont JC and ending walking across the stage with our degrees as teachers. One time, I called her while she was in the middle of class, and she picked up the phone, spoke to me, and checked one of her students at the same time. During the L.A. riots, the city was on lockdown, and that's how she became pregnant. "My daughter's dad and his girlfriend started tripping at my nana's funeral when we had the after party in her backyard. I was like 'Look. I was going to fuck Puppet from down the street, but we weren't allowed to leave the house, so I ended up fucking your dumbass.' I told his girl that I didn't want him. I'm finer than her anyways. That bitch still wanted to fight. Bitch, I put myself through college with a kid. I'm over his ass. My *tias* saw what was going down and jumped out of their lawn chairs with the 40 oz in their brown bag. The dominoes scattered on the grass. Puppet stood in between us. That bitch backed down real quick. People will push you around if you let them. You feel me, bitch?"

That night, I went home and dismantled my wardrobe, getting rid of the clothes that made me look 60 years old and replacing them with the ones that made me feel like I was in my 20s. Cotton underwear were replaced with thongs, flats with high heels, baggy jeans with booty grabbers, painted toes and matching nails, Eternity perfume, bubble baths, and cherry candles. I bought a pink teddy to wear around my house just to feel sexy for myself, and if I didn't want to wear a bra that day, I was fine letting my girls dangle freely. I didn't like the idea of being confined to a man-made elastic strap that cut off my blood circulation. The tit sling as I called it. I cut off my long black hair and made plans for my next tattoo. I began working out, attending heated Pilates class six days a week, losing 40 lbs. My jean size shrunk from a size twelve to a size four.

Chola was harsh with the way she showed her love, but she was right. I grew tired of falling asleep with my tears and listening to depressing songs on repeat just to feel sorry for myself. I needed that kick in the ass to start the process of loving myself, instead of searching for love in all the wrong places. I'd be a fool if I said I had no clue he was seeing Monica, again. She was always his "go to" side chick. When his demeanor changed and the intimacy stopped, I knew something was up. Knowing his temper, I was hesitant to confront him with one piece of evidence. I began stacking a case against him, and I put on my poker face pretending I knew nothing. The $100 receipts to restaurants and bars around town, the emails to Monica following up after their date to the drive-in, the relationship memes sent to his phone, the countdown on his calendar when I was leaving town for business were small bricks to my case. So when I was out of town and I received the butt dialed phone call, I stopped thinking and finally shouted the words that were in me all along, "Get the fuck out," and when I said them, I never returned to the old me.

CHAPTER TWENTY-SEVEN
BEAUTIFUL THERAPY

"Si yo quiero un pinche hombre, me lo compro," Doña Guera said to her family who scold her because of her masculine ways, "if I want a fucking man, I'll buy him."

"You can't buy a man, mom," her children insisted, but she did, and at 72 years old, she bought the strongest man to please her in bed. Doña Guera owned all the bars and more than half the restaurants in the state of Sinaloa. The *puebla* knew who to ask if they needed money for food, clothes, or to pay off a debt, but it came with a cost of endless adjectives of name calling if they didn't pay their dues. Even if a cop pulled her over, his ass was the sorry one.

"Hijo de tu puta madre," she cursed as she rolled down the passenger window, her chauffeur keeping quiet at all times. The cop searched inside her Rolls Royce with a flashlight, his hand cocked around his pistol, *"Desculpa me, Doña Guera. No sabia que era ti,"* his palm trembled as he pardoned himself for his mistake, "excuse me. I didn't know it was you."

"You saw U.S. license plates and thought you would fuck with my money, you son of a bitch. Fuck you and your mother. Where's the

10,000 *pesos* you owe me, asshole?" Doña Guera lashed out in Spanish, piercing her eyes through the cop's balls. She instructed her driver to speed off leaving the cop covered in dirt.

"*Tu puta madre*" jumped out her mouth before she opened her eyes to start her day. Her breakfast was served, on time, *chilaquiles verdes* with caramelized beans, a secret recipe passed down from her father that was on the menu at all of Doña Guera's restaurants. She sipped on the ripest *tequila*, the blue agave plant harvest to satisfy her taste buds. Her bubble bath sprinkled with hand-picked rose petals prepared each morning after breakfast. Midday four servants were scheduled for Doña Guera's massage and facial all at her disposal. When she stepped into any room, the energy shifted towards her, everyone lining up to kiss her hand or her ass.

Her father was an old-school mafioso, who raised his daughter to play like a man. By the time she was in grade school, she knew how to load pistols and sharpen knives while the other girls played hopscotch. Doña Guera was trained early to keep her mouth shut if anyone asked about her father. She dressed better than her classmates, including the children of Mexico's president. Her catholic school dresses were imported from Italy, her shoes sparkled in gold with each step she planted into the earth. Three security guards were instructed to escort her throughout the day, and teachers never assigned her homework, so that she spent quality time with her father. Doña Guera learned to keep track of the books and collected debt from those who owed. She learned to make a man feel small, tucking his tail between his ass. They knew not to touch her, just obey, be a good little boy, and hand over the money. As she kept track of the books, she memorized clients' by name, address, and phone number. No man dared pass a lie through Doña Guera, and when her father passed, she became the wealth for the people.

Although tough by environment, Doña Guera shared a soft spot for her grandson, Jesse. When asked who was her favorite, she responded, "*Ese cabron con los pinche ojos verdes,*" Jesse's green eyes reminding her of her father. As a child, Jesse traveled from San Diego to visit his grandmother during the summers.

"My grandmother had deeper balls than the dudes in her town. She was the only one who could tell a cop to kick rocks," Jesse said aligning caps of ink on his glass table, "check out my new machine. The technology they are coming up with is crazy. It's much lighter than my old one." He picked up the needle and dipped it into the ink. "Are you ready?" He stretched the needle across my skin as he continued with his story, "I was fucking scared. I was only 11 years old in the backseat with her. We were on our way to the circus, but the lights flashed behind us. I thought we were going to get arrested." Jesse began digging in my forearm. When I was browsing through a book, an old postcard of Frida Kahlo floated from the pages. Ralph mailed me postcards even if he didn't go out of town. For this particular case, he sent it because I was hired as an English teacher at San Diego High, the postcard dated 2007. Ten years later, it surfaced back around at the right time. Whenever I overcame a tough period in my life, I rewarded myself with a tattoo. I was running out of room. In the picture, Frida's face was soft her arms crossed, and her body wrapped in a shawl, beautiful jewelry pressed against her neck and fingers. I became most inspired by her when Ralph and I traveled to Mexico City visiting the infamous *Casita Azul,* the little blue house. Each wall in its own color, its own world; crochet pillows with her and Diego's name; used paint brushes; wooden beds; and a healing garden with a replica Aztec pyramid. Jessie always had a story in mind every time he inked me, whether it was an insane girlfriend driving her car through her cheating boyfriend's garage or breaking his car windows for calling her a *pendeja,* an idiot. Jesse was not only a tattoo artist, but he was also a storyteller, and I listened.

"That summer, I got hooked up. I always wanted a canary. They sold them at the shop down the street. Dude who owned the shop was suspicious of me at first."

"Can I help you?"

"I want a bird, but I don't have any money."

"Then, I can't help you."

"My grandma said to take it off the money you owe her." The man froze in his tracks, slowly removing the toothpick from his mouth.

"Doña Guera is your grandmother? Tell her I take good care of you, my friend."

"Dude was nice all quick. He showed me around the shop. I picked an exotic bird and was given a cage and food. He bought me ice cream afterwards and then escorted me back to my grandma's house. My grandma was a cold piece even if dudes were all nice to her."

"*Doña Guera, ayude a tu nieto*," Canary man bragged how much he helped her grandson.

"*Mira cabron. Hijo de tu puta madre. Todavia me debes dinero,*" Doña Guera shouted as she inhaled a puff of her Cuban cigar, "you son of a bitch. You still owe me money." She was tanning by her pool, her legs spread revealing nature's gift. Canary man bowed his head in shame, as she yanked out a part of his soul and dick at the same time. It didn't matter how hard the men tried, she always greeted them with curse words, insults of their mother, followed by the questioning of her money. Doña Guera put down the Cuban cigar and began sipping on her wine, "Are you happy with your fucking bird?" Jesse shook his head to show his content for his bird. "Go to fucking hell, and get the fuck out of my face," she screamed throwing her wine glass at Canary Man.

"My grandma's place was the spot for the summer. I took advantage of that shit. I went to the *Lucha Libre* that traveled to town. The wrestling show was for men only. When I approached the counter, a man whispered to the cashier, who looked at me, and then looked away, and then back at me. They had a special seat for me in the front row of the wrestling ring. I was assigned a waiter who stood next to me for the entire event. I ordered popcorn, pizza, soda, all the good shit. When my grandma passed, she left everything to her boyfriend and one house to me, but I didn't want the house. I gave it to my uncle. My family was pissed."

The ink traced my skin, outlining Frida's famous unibrow, "Why do you think she did that?" I asked. Jesse stopped his machine, his eyes focused in the moment. After Doña Guera's funeral, her family argued for months, brothers throwing things at each other, aunts slapping their nieces. Tension grew so much within the family that trips were made to the hospital. Doña Guera's son stabbed his cousin on his shoulder. Paramedics, police, and helicopters were called to Doña Guera's mansion, her family wasting the town's resources. Jesse nodded his head back and forth before looking up, "To teach us a lesson." He started his machine and finished my tattoo.

CHAPTER TWENTY-EIGHT

UNDOCUMENTED VALEDICTORIAN

After my breakup with him, I searched for my childhood memories to make sense of who I was, attempting to regain my forgotten past when I was too busy tangled in that spiderweb of a relationship. The presidential campaign was all over the news, debates, scandals, insults to Mexicans accused of being rapist and murders. That triggered my mind, and Rafa popped in my head. With a few Google searches, I was able to find Rafa's social media page, and that's how we reconnected.

Rafa and I rode the bus together from Logan Heights to the beach community where we dropped off to receive a so-called higher education. I was quiet and observed him daily. Rafa always carried a book in his hand, which where we came from was rather uncommon, even brave. One day, he read about Che and the Cuban revolution, or Plato, or *A Hundred Years of Solitude*, all the philosophers, the ideas trapped in his head. He had a barrio story, like the rest of us.

Coming from Logan Heights traveling across town, we were already viewed as the underprivileged, the poor, the illegals, the Welfare recipients, the nobodies. Stepping off the bus, we all wore used clothes and pondered the whereabouts of our next meal. It's easy for school not to be a priority, when dodging bullets was more imperative than studying vocabulary. The survival of the fittest in a country that already sets one up for failure for those who wander from another land.

"I almost fell in the trap flunking out my freshman year. I was spending time in the streets. My mother didn't know anything about school, and I didn't have a father. I had poor attendance showing up to school only fifteen days of one hundred." A typical Mexican scenario one might argue. At 5 years old, Rafa migrated to the U.S. from his homeland of Morelia, Michoacán, his mother sneaking him across the border in the middle of the night and a father left behind as a distant memory. We ordered a couple of API blonde beers, and he shared his journey to this country. We have a false ideology about the American dream that we see on the big screens. *Gringos* portrayed as Latinos as their audience yearns to fit the status quo, and yet we fall for such perception that somewhere growing up, we lose sight of ourselves.

Rafa joined the cross-country team, knowing his shift in academics needed change.

Already one of the top runners in the county, he became the San Diego champion his sophomore year, "Everyone looked at me, and said this guy is stupid. I'm not that. I'm going to prove to you guys that I can do that as well. I wanted to get a scholarship through running or academics." Esmeralda Nava was a classmate and teammate, who had all AP classes and accepted to Harvard, Stanford, and Princeton, all the top schools. Perfect scores on the SAT. "She inspired me. From there on, I said I was going to kick ass in academics." She told me, 'You can make it, however, you want to go.' Everyone was so far ahead. It took a lot of reading and catching up. I studied math books on my own." By his junior year, Rafa had read almost everything that was out there. "A book that changed my life was a social philosophy book. It's called *The Jungle*. It's about the meat packing industry in Chicago. That whole movement of the poor, the rich, and the division of classes really hit home. The poor are always going to be poor, and the rich are always going to be rich. How do you overcome that? I was trying to get out of it myself. Not to become rich but to become successful. The power of an idea and that you can't destroy. Once you let that out, you can change the world. Just reading the right book made the difference." Biology and chemistry fascinated Rafa, and he eventually left his cross-country team to focus on his academics. When he applied to colleges and was asked for his social security number, Rafa left it blank, a realization that now confronted him. It didn't matter if he earned straight A's in advanced courses, volunteered in the community, or voted the president of all the clubs on campus. He went through with the application process anyways and was accepted by a few of the colleges. "I was interviewed by Princeton, and I was surprised that the University of Chicago offered me a full ride. I had no other means of financial aid. Then, there was my status. I was illegal." It painted a story that it was a good accomplishment to get there, but in the end, you don't belong in this country. "I didn't come to this country. It wasn't my fault. I didn't break the law. I didn't have the conscious mind or mobility to come cross. I was a migrant, and now, I'm in this predicament. All that time I grew up here. That's where the struggle is. The struggle of being undocumented, being discriminated against. Always viewed as a second-class citizen. I was always feeling less."

We live in a society that already displays a negative stigma against undocumented immigrants, against the poor. Whoever has the most, whoever has the highest degree, whoever dresses in designer clothing, lives in the mansion, drives the Lamborghini *es el mas chingón,* the biggest hot shot. Now being illegal, undocumented, and Mexican is even worse. That is the real struggle. "I had to prove that I was capable, that I belonged here. Competition didn't end once I'm valedictorian. Now, I'm competing with the top students in this institution. They also have the back up from their parents and the funding. They have the advantage to begin with. I was competing constantly against that."

Rafa's deportation trial was suspended after an attorney heard about his case and worked for pro bono. Rafa turned himself into INS and presented his case to the immigration judge. There are three fundamental criteria that allowed a person to stay in the U.S.: you are a person of good moral character, you have extreme economic hardship, and you have ties to the United States. "What backed me up were my academics. When my academics were presented, that demonstrated that I had potential above and beyond the normal criteria."

The story hasn't changed. Over twenty years later, many students struggled to stay in a country they called home. The mentality of a country that builds walls, preventing immigrants to enter and live a modest life, was unsettling. "The fact that someone in a position of power is thinking about that is disturbing as well. Someone that can actually make laws and try to change things. It's going to impact a lot of people. This whole Donald Trump thing. Governor Pete Wilson tried to pass Proposition 187. Let's get all these undocumented children and kick them out. What people miss is the economical impact of immigrants. Do they take Welfare? Some of them do. Do they take medical services? Some of them do. That's insignificant in comparison to the contribution that they bring to the economy. Every immigrant becomes a consumer. By becoming a consumer, you drive economic growth. You have to buy food. You have to pay rent. You create your own place in society. They don't receive money back when they pay taxes. It stays with the federal government. So under that situation, they are not taking from society. When have you seen a freckled face American serve you your bean burrito or work in the fields? You haven't."

Rafa has published research and developed patents for the advancement of science in order to find a cure for a disease or a diagnosis of a disease to develop the products. Rafa raised three children, owns several properties, and has one hundred and forty men and women working under him.

I recalled his struggles and remembered watching him on the news. I pointed to the television and shouted, "I know him. He rides the bus with me." How could one immigrant from Barrio Logan out hustle the rich kids from Point Loma, who had private tutors, computers, violin lessons, and trust funds? Survive or die.

Reconnecting with Rafa helped me viewed my struggles in a different perspective. There was no shame where I grew up. To tell you the truth, my problems were petty. A writer from Malibu agreed to cover Rafa's story, heard about it in the news, and made the drive to interview him. However, the interview never took place, and Rafa's story was left untold for years. Rafa and I smiled at each other from across the table, raising our beers, "*Salud*, my brother. Your story will be shared with the world."

CHAPTER TWENTY-NINE

MI BARRIO THROUGH THE YEARS

Word of mouth spread quickly that a group of white supremacists planned to defaced the murals at Chicano Park because they were frantic that their Confederate statues were threatened to be removed throughout the U.S., and this was their proper recourse of action. The nationalist caused chaos in Charlottesville, Virginia causing a riot, killing a lady, and injuring other people of color who resisted injustice. The neo-Nazis attempted to create the same absurdity in Logan Heights, *mi barrio.*

The summer of 2012, Nayeli, Monse, and I painted a mural as part of the Chicano Park restoration project. We participated with the older women, who were the original muralists back when the city of San Diego scheduled to build a police station on our land. On April 22nd, 1970, the community of Logan Heights united to fight for a park, digging holes to plant trees, blocking bulldozers, and forming human chains. My uncles and father were protesters, a responsibility of activism they now passed on to me. The day the white supremacist strategized to eradicate the park they, too, were met with the same people, as well as the newer generation who raised against oppression. Nayeli, born in Michoacán and majoring as an engineer at UCSD, wore her custom-made indigenous jewelry; Monse, born in Mexico City and served in the U.S. Navy, wore her Mexican embroidered blouse; and me, *la pocha*, wore a t-shirt that read *Desde La Logan* in old English lettering, each with our own unique barrio style. We met at Salud, a new tacos spot that used to be the old Porkyland, and then we walked a few blocks to our destination. Most of the local businesses were replaced with businesses that generated more revenue geared towards modernization. The only thing that still remained authentic was Chicano Park. Police officers were in full force, and the Chicano Park Steering Committee wrote a letter as a reminder to stand in solidarity and not display any form of violent acts. Over 500 people came together to protect the murals, forming a circle around each one. A native man blew on his ocean shell that warned us the group had arrived. We quickly took our stance, fist in the air, like an army ready for battle. Nayeli, Monse, and I guarded our mural, Women Hold up Half the Sky, along with a group of *Pachucos* who traveled from Los Angeles to support the cause. There were different forms of Mexicans: the *Pachucos*, the rastas with dreads, the *Zapatistas*, the bikers, the homies in lowriders, the natives, and the Brown Berets.

"Get out of our park!"

"We will fight back!"

"We are here to protect our indigenous land!"

"Afuera! Afuera! Leave! Leave!"

Flags from Latin American countries soared high. The group was confronted by power and resistance. On September 3rd, 2017, racism did not win. The blue line shield the nationalist for protection and eventually escorted them off the premises, the crowd cheering in victory as they left. My uncles' song playing from the *quiosco*, *"We shall continue to live my brother. We shall continue to fight my friend. For Chicano Park. Under the bridge."* The day we stood up to white supremacists, Trump put a halt to DACA recipients, and I realized the fight wasn't over. Nayeli was in the process of becoming a citizen through DACA. Her son was a US citizen, and I was torn that if she was removed from the only country she knew, where would her son go?

Walking back to my car after the event settled down, I had parked across the street from my old bus stop, which was in front of a two-story white house, the same bus stop where Rafa and I waited each morning. Since the house I grew up in was only a block away, I cruised down memory lane. The house on Julian Ave was no longer brown and yellow but blue with an American flag and Rottweiler guarding the property. An old man slowly approached the screen door when he noticed me loitering outside his property.

"Can I help you?"

"I grew up in this house."

He thought for a minute, "You're Maria's daughter."

"Yes. She's my mother." I explained that I was at the park for the protest and decided to come revisit my old house since I was in the neighborhood. I asked about childhood friends. They all moved out of Logan and up north starting their families, working their typical 9-5 jobs. Jaime was working for the city, and his brother, Chonie, was a deputy. Their mother, my nina, moved to Murrieta. The house, for the most part, was what I remembered, the porch paint still chipped, paradise flowers in the yard, an apricot tree, and the driveway where I dribble my basketball.

I thought about my conversation with Rafa, how we discussed growing up in our community over the years. Some good, some bad. Although the neighborhood was different in some aspects, the people were still willing to protect their land even if they moved miles away. As I stood outside my old house on Julian Ave, I was reminded that the little girl in me, once lost, found her way back home.

CHAPTER THIRTY
MINERVA

Of course, with every victory comes a celebration. Minerva invited the homegirls to her pad in celebration of her birthday and our victory at the park. The group huddled into her cozy apartment tucked away in a cul-de-sac. Her place flooded with books by Black and Brown authors: Tomas Rivera, Junot Díaz, Alice Walker, Roberto Bolano, and Assata Shakur. A postcard from Cuba of *Comandante* Che, and *"Viva La Mujer"* etched on her wall.

"Fuck Walk Whitman," Minerva shouted as she leaped on her couch and raised her wine glass, "Tupac is America's greatest poet." We rapped to *Live and Die in L.A.*, "Go hard or go home. We shall never get used for our oppression," Minerva announced before emptying her glass, "giving up is not in our blood." A border child who sold *cafésitos* of *canela* and chocolate at her mother's coffeehouse, once not able to speak English, was now a candidate for the Ph.D. program at UCSD, "English is that bull I learned to dominate. To unleash whatever necessary. Fuck you, colonialism." If there was a protest in San Diego, Minerva was front and center resisting political oppression and gentrification in our neighborhoods.

I met Minerva back when we were students at the local junior colleges. We worked in the ESL department at O'Farrell Middle

School, located in Encanto, a predominately Black and Latino neighborhood, teaching migrant students to read and write at grade level or else they would be labeled as "far below basic" and placed in special needs classes. We taught there for many years until there weren't enough funds in the budget, the district terminating our positions and programs. Even after we both earned our college degrees, we kept in touch discussing books and events in the political world. We swapped ideas for lesson plans that geared towards our student population as we were now both college professors and guest lecturing in each other's class. When Uncle Chunky's wife wrote a letter to the community to protest my first book, Minerva debated with other professors in her department, standing her ground, challenging those who banned my book. The true dagger in my heart was seeing Uncle Chunky's signature attached to that letter. Because I wrote my book, Uncle Chunky and I no longer spoke to each other even up to his death.

As the night progressed, Minerva kicked off her high heels and danced in a circle, shaking her ass like J.Lo in her videos. Minerva was thick in all the right places, slipping her apple shaped ass into a skin tight vintage velvet dress with a pearl choker, her kinky hair loose, like a wild woman. The men broke their necks every time she'd walk down the street. I pulled out a couple of bills flicking them her way, and the other girls followed my lead. I joined her with my own twerking, and she grind me from behind smacking my hips. I finally laughed. A female couple locked lips and squeezed each other's breast, free to do so against the world outside. Minerva took it back old school and played a video of D'Angelo, the one where he is only wearing a gold chain and his cornrows.

"Minerva, you need to turn that shit off or else I'll start fucking you. Call me a queer if it makes you feel better to judge," I announced.

"It's your short hair, sleeve tattoos, and attitude," Minerva added.

"Thanks for the compliment, *mija*. You trying to get in my pants? You won't be the first girl I've kissed." We joked like women do when they're free and single, releasing our feminine energy that wept inside us for generations, sad stories past down from our great-great-grandmothers who rode horses in search of a husband, so the myth goes, but by the time those played out stories arrived within us, we're like, nah homegirl, we're good. We don't need a man to fulfill our happiness. *Y las mujeres* danced in a circle celebrating our victory, our queerness, our womanhood, and our freedom from the stories and people who tried to oppress us but failed.

CHAPTER THIRTY-ONE

10:00 P.M. CALL

It started as a typical evening for me, taking Zach out to the bathroom and washing the dishes before I went to bed. Due to Zach's arthritis, I lifted him as he plopped down at the foot my bed, stretching his body, leaving me very little room. Doing my best, I slipped between the sheets. I began to place my phone on my nightstand, but it rang in the palm of my hand at 10:00 p.m. on the dot. The number was not saved on my contacts, but it was a number I would remember always. I was hesitant to pick up, so I let it ring a few times before I answered.

"Hello," I said with uncertainty.

A long pause and breathing waited at the other end, "It's me, Jason."

"I know who it is."

"I need to speak with you." He spoke in a monotone voice, a voice that didn't belong to him. It appeared that he had cried for quite some time before calling.

"What's going on?"

"I need to speak with you," he cleared his throat, "in person."

"I'm free now."

"No," he said slowly, "not now. I need to see you in person. I need you to do something you might not be willing to do."

"J, you don't sound too good."

"I'm not," he mumbled, "I really need to speak with you in person soon."

"I can meet Saturday."

"We can meet at Colima Park by the kid's playground."

"Ok. I'll see you in a few days."

It took a while to let the call digest into my system. By now, I was wide awake with a million thoughts running through my head. I called Scott, who had known Jason since junior high. Scott informed me that Jason knew about the book. He read the experts I posted online, as I imagined he would.

I placed my phone back on my nightstand, setting my alarm for dawn, so I could begin my morning writing. I glanced at the calendar tacked to my wall. It was one year to the date that Jason and I broke up. Some may call me crazy for agreeing to meet with him. Emotions run high and anyone is capable of anything when they aren't thinking, and emotions are heavily invested.

What will happen on Saturday? I thought to myself. I didn't know, but I was willing to find out because the truth must be told. This wasn't the first time someone tried to stop me from writing. When I wrote my first book, I was invited to a local event at the Centro Cultural de La Raza to display my book. With my luck, my cousin, Nando's sister, was there and phoned her mother, the witch, who arrived minutes later, interrupting the event, slamming my books on the ground in disgust. The public pulled out their cell phones to take pictures or to record the scandalous act. If I went through that and made it out, I could go through this. Fear left me a year ago when I found myself. Fear is only the meaning we give it. People live their lives in fear. Fear to be great, fear of beliefs, fear that someone looks different from us or prays differently. Fear of losing someone. Fear of honesty. Fear to be average. Fear to change. Whatever drives us, fear plays a factor. Good or bad. I give fear no meaning because I know that if it knocks me down, I will get back up and stare it in the face as many times as it takes.

CHAPTER THIRTY-TWO

CALL TO THE VIRG

"Are you out of your fucking mind? The park? That's rule 101. Never meet at a park. What's your problem?"

"Wait. Wait. Wait. Don't answer. I know your problem. You're a woman. That's the problem with women in their 20's, 30's, and 40's. You go off emotion."

"I have a thirty year head start on you. You know what I would've told him? Go fuck yourself, asshole. I've moved on."

"Who have you told?"

"Ok, so the whole fucking world knows already."

"I don't know what goes on in that head of yours. This has got to be the stupidest thing you've ever done, and you have done some stupid shit. You're smart and stupid at the same time."

"Here we go again. Every time you write a book half the fucking world wants to kill you."

"Oh spare me your final epic battle bullshit. No, it's not like Harry Potter vs. Lord Voldemort. This is real life."

"No shit it didn't work out with his side bitch. She's a fucking cheater like him."

"I have to worry about you. I'm your aunt. Someone has to worry about you because you don't worry about yourself."

"Yes, I'd feel a lot better if you met there instead."

"Hold on Trump and Kim Jong Un are on TV arguing and calling each other a bunch of names. They should get married. I don't care if they blow up the world. They're funny. We have two comedians running their countries. They should go on a comedy tour. Blow us all up, fuckers, and put us out of our misery. I'm not even scared anymore. Ha!"

"That's right assholes. Push that button. I'm not going to put up with this shit for another three years. Blow us up, now. Trump likes to fight, like when he went to that MMA."

"Whatever the fuck it was. WWE then. If Jesus Christ came down on a cross, he'd fight with him."

"I wondered how much he's paying Melania to stay married to him."

"I should go on tour and talk shit about Trump. I can't look any stupider than him."

"No, I don't believe you."

"The Chargers lost again. What they ought to do is bring in an Indian tribe or a *curandera* and sprinkle smoke on them or whatever the fuck they do. Everyone needs to be there coaches, players, trainers, the mascot, locker room assistants. While they're at it, they can sprinkle holy water on Trump, too. Cleanse that asshole. In fact, cleanse the whole Goddamn country, and call it a National Day of Cleansing. We can tell families to take the most miserable person in their family, the one nobody wants to invite to parties, like your dad. Take that asshole to the cleansing."

"Hold on again. Trump is holding a press conference so we'll have a bunch of stupid shit to talk about tomorrow."

"I need to laugh and watch this shit. Don't do anything stupid. Bye."

Click.

CHAPTER THIRTY-THREE

FINAL GOODBYE

I pulled into the parking lot of the Living Room Cafe around 5:00 p.m. I shuffled through my purse and adjust my mirror to apply my lipstick and check my hair. The jeans and high heels I ordered on Amazon arrived today, so I chose to wear my new gear for the meeting. As I helped Zach out of the back seat, I received a text, "I'm across the street at the mortuary." In a distance, Jason appeared small, slouching on a curb with his hands over his head. I sighed before I walked with Zach across the street. Crows cried in the sky. The background noise was loud, cars passing, homeless people yelling at themselves, kids riding their bikes, but my mind became silenced. The mortuary parking lot was empty, and the cast iron doors were bolted shut. As I stepped my way closer, Jason cleared this throat scrambling through his backpack, pulling out a folder.

"I don't know where to begin." He cleared his throat again, "You can read this, I suppose." I sat beside him as he handed me a torn page from a notebook. Zach greeted Jason, wagging his little nugget of a tail as I took my time carefully reading each sentence, each word, each syllable. I handed it back when I was finished. "Are you done?"

"Yes, I read the whole thing."

"The story is not even what I am. The story how I got this way," Jason paused. We both watched a city bus driving by to pass some time. "If you are going to bring down the hammer, you might as well bring it down. Do you want help?"

"Help with what?"

"What's in my head. It's something that is God awful. I never talked about it with anybody before, not even my brothers. My mom knows some of it. It's part of the reason she is the way she is, the way I am. I know what's coming out," Jason folded the letter in half and placed it in his backpack, "and it's raw. All I ask is that you give me a three week head start."

"For what?"

"Before the book comes out."

"What do you mean a three week head start?"

"Just let me know three weeks before it comes out."

"Why?"

"So I can plan accordingly."

"It's coming out on my birthday. What are you going to do, J?"

"I can't tell you about that. It carries too much of a burden that I don't fit in anymore. What you know is nothing compared to what I know. What is your goal with me? To humiliate me?"

"This is my therapy."

"I'm not trying to stop you or anything. You are owning your craft. That's how you heal. I encourage that." Jason's voice shook. This was the first time it was soft and easy to listen to. "You have no idea the unbelievable strength I have now, and although you did put me through some shit, I wouldn't trade it for anything."

Jason broke down and sobbed as he trembled back into his hands, "I have done God awful things to you. There's no way I can take away that physical pain."

"It's not too late to start over on yourself. The pain you're going through, I already went through last year. There were times when I went home and fell to the ground crying, and I stayed there for hours. I listen to every depressing song you could think of, and I just cried. I cried all day, all night, so I know what you're going through. But if you make it out, I promise you will be a better person."

Jason cried harder.

"Did you have a shitty past and a shitty upbringing? Show me someone who had the perfect life. We can either choose the path of destruction or we can choose the path of bettering ourselves, and that's what I choose. I think you should continue on that path, too. I surrounded myself with people who were supportive, strong women, women that have been through it. Not only women who have been in my situation but rose above it. Now, I can say I did that. I'm not the same person I was when we broke up, but I had to go through those ten years with you and experience the pain to find myself and find the strength that I didn't know I had. With every bad in the relationship, I have to thank you for the good because you prepared me for anything that comes my way. I no longer fear because I know I can overcome it. And I have to thank you for that. The year that has gone by, with the self-reflection I have done on myself, my mistakes, my fault as a person. I'm not perfect either. To the next person that comes in my life, I'm going to be a better person, and I hope that the next person that comes in your life, you'll be a better person, too."

"I have a lot of respect for you. I am ashamed of myself for the way I treated you."

"So why did you call me?"

"I just came to offer you the story you don't know about. I lost my passion, my zest. If you really want to dig me in, I wanted to help you. That way at least people will understand. I wish that me being short, fat, bald, and broke where the worse things about me. I've condemned myself with who I am now. I owe you the credibility. I owe you a lot, and I will never get to repay you. I wanted to offer it to you, but once it's out, there's no turning back."

"Why are you speaking like this?"

"I just don't see any redemption. I feel like the damage is done. Everything you said is right. Everything about me is right. I'm not deserving. I'm already damaged like I did to you. I want that kind of punishment to feel, at least, a little bit even. You got the worse of me, and you still loved me."

"And I will always love you."

"I wouldn't trade our time together either. I don't know how to describe it. I'm such a disaster. You didn't deserve any of that. I wish I was so much better for you. You're so talented, so bright, driven, hardworking, focused. I took away from that. I feel like I clipped a bird's wings."

"But my wings grew back, and they grew back stronger."

"I am so sorry," the sincerity in his eyes was truthful, asking for forgiveness, "I admire you. Everyone told me I should be upset, but I was proud of you. I got contacted by tons of people, text, calling me asking if I knew what was out there. I know you're strong. I know how talented you are. Just the power you could do with the pen. If anyone was going to not hate me, but look at me differently or laugh or anything like that, it was well deserved. If I didn't want you to say those things, I should've been better to you. I knew I wouldn't be able to hold my tears today. I saw your post, and I sat there and cried like a little bitch. It's okay because you are real, raw. You don't hide. You're not afraid. It wasn't without its affects, though. For me, I need to step back and reevaluate my life. That's good. Without your words. They were eye opening. I always looked at coaching as a good thing. I always thought that was something good that I was doing."

"You're a good coach."

"Not anymore I'm not."

"Quit?"

"Resigned. It's a waste of time. What was I doing that for? Why was I there in the first place?"

"It brought value to your life at the time."

"Had you told me that sooner I might have been upset that maybe I wouldn't have agreed. It was a different time in my life. I can see that maybe I was chasing something that I never had. That I really never needed. I thought it was important. I had my job there, coaching, and building something. I was grateful that you made me think what I was doing. You made me focus on something bigger. Coaching is selfish, I guess, as funny as that sounds. You could only do so much being a coach. It might not have grasp my attention how minuscule, kind of petty coaching one team is. It took the focus off what I was doing, and

130

it made me focus on something a little bigger. I appreciate that. Your honesty has always been your incredible virtue. That hasn't changed."

We chuckled together for the first time since our breakup, a moment that we both appreciated.

"You might have changed a lot of things, but your best quality is what makes you who you are, and it really shines through. People are scared of that. People are scared of stepping on toes. When they ask people who are near death what they would have done different if given more time, they always say, 'I wish I was more honest with myself. I wish I gave less consideration to what people think.' It's not going to be the way you answer that question. Not me. I care too much of what people think. It takes away from life."

Jason rubbed a tear from his eye. I noticed his nails weren't cut. I always gave him a manicure after a long week of wrestling practice. All the admirable things we did for each other popped into my brain. The breakfast sandwiches he made for me; our trip to Yosemite, how he pushed me to reach the top of Half Dome when I wanted to give up; the times we threw monster rolls at the craps table; attending Paul McCartney's concert at the MGM; our camping trip throughout Baja California; even something so simple like waking up next to him and Zach made me happy. For the first time in a long time, I saw Jason as human.

"What else are you working on? I know you're not working on just one thing." I shared the Chicano Park children's book pending and how my friend, Sunny Rey, and I were still writing our book on the homeless guy, Craig Miller, we found dead on Christmas day. From here, our conversation became more casual, more friendly. We talked about how we changed our eating habits, quit drinking, exercised more, books we read, career moves, and family.

"Sorry to hear about your uncle's passing."

"Thank you."

"How's everyone doing? Ralph, Virg, Rick?"

"Virg is still cussing at Donald Trump through the T.V. Rick is retired and drinking more vodka, and Ralph is roaming the streets of City Heights."

"Are they still Charger fans?" We both shared another laugh.

"They just watch football for the sake of watching football. I'm trying to repair my relationship with my mom. For the first time in many years, I bought her a birthday present, Eternity perfume, her favorite. She was actually surprised."

"Me, too. My mom had a heart attack and had triple bypass surgery. I was the only one she would let see. I bought her a pillow and blanket when she was in the hospital. It was probably the happiest she had been in years. I'm happy for you. Thank you for coming to see me."

"Of course."

"It was good to get that stuff off my chest."

"I hope you feel better."

"It's a process. I guess."

"You'll be fine. You'll be strong. I made it through and so will you. This might sound weird, but my intentions for writing this was to not embarrass you, but hopefully, you would see and in turn, make yourself a better person."

"I've done a lot of uncontrollable crying. I have breakdowns everywhere, at work, just walking."

"As soon as you love yourself—that's what I was working on—and you gotta do that, too. When you do that, great things are going to happen in your life. I said I wasn't the same person I was a year ago, and you don't have to be either. We can either look for the wrong things that are going on or all the right things that are happening. Anybody can choose."

"Life is crazy. I'm definitely working on my health. You saw how much I was drinking. I was drinking a fifth of vodka a night. I was dying. I was smoking, popping pills. Things get masked by substances so there's nowhere to hide. It's easier to take your mind off stuff when you've a pint of vodka deep, stoned, and playing video games. It's easy not to think about life. It's a lot more thinking when your head is clear. A lot more reflective. You kind of realize what you've done. That part is tough, but it's not too tough where I feel like picking up a bottle. It scared me. I was a full blown alcoholic and didn't even realize it."

"But the important thing is that you did. Most people choose to continue."

"A lot of productiveness is gone at the bottom of the bottle. If I have my health and save my sanity, I'll be okay."

"I promise you, you'll be okay."

"Time heals all wounds, *que no*? And you had to go make me that damn *chorizo* sandwich."

Jason patted Zach on his paw, "You're still the only one who he allows to touch his paw. He won't let anyone else do it." We took Zach for a stroll around the block before heading back to my car. Jason lifted Zach in the back seat and shut the door.

"Thank you for seeing me. It was good to see you and Zach." Jason stepped towards me, and we embraced our final goodbye hug. We held each other tight, and I sunk my head into his chest, hearing our hearts beat together.

"Good luck with your book coming out."

With tears in both our eyes, we let go of each other, and as we slowly released, the new Vera smiled at Jason, and the new Jason smiled back.

CHAPTER THIRTY-FOUR

PHILIPPIANS 4:13

Let me first say that I am sorry. I need to forgive you, forgive myself, and lift this weight off my shoulders. The only way for me to move on is for me to forgive and accept love. The pair makes me strong, and I must move on from the past, rebuilding myself and the relationships that were broken. I'm tired of pointing fingers; you did this; you did that. I fell into the trap of my parents; the cycle continued, but I can't blame them, and I can't blame you. I am responsible for my happiness. The world, the universe, is working for me, not against me. The brick wall that I build has now come down, and I finally embrace the feeling of love that was in front of me the whole time. The feeling of family; the feeling of laughter; the feeling to cry because with tears comes smiles. You brought out the scared little girl who hid from herself through pain, that so-called tough act, but she is nurtured now and ready to better herself because when I am happy and at peace, I can give that back to the world.

Everyone is deserving of forgiveness, and more importantly, deserving of love. Don't judge people based on who they were. People have the power to change. Why do we argue with ourselves, beat ourselves up in our head, and go to war with ourselves? We battle daily with ourselves, closed off accepting who we are, forgetting that we are great human beings who just want to be loved, but truth is, we have to love ourselves first. Within ourselves, we can be kind to our inner being so in turn, we can give that love back, whether it be to our partner, parents, children, family, even a complete stranger cleaning windows at a gas station, or a hippie lady with missing body parts. Nobody is perfect, and we don't have to be, but everyone should be capable of love. This world needs more of it. Understanding self-importance is the most powerful gift we can give ourselves because within understanding who we are, we can finally begin the process of love. But at some point in our lives, we must experience the pain. Some make it out alive, and some don't, unfortunately. Did I love my cousin Nando? With all my heart. Was Uncle Chunky loved? By the world. Did they love themselves? I don't know. Some people live a lifetime never loving themselves even in their final moments. Robin Williams made everyone laugh, except himself. This world could use less judgment and more love.

My aunt and friends called me crazy. Don't do it; don't trust him; be careful; be where there are a lot of people. My family and friends worried that you would try to do something to me, cut me up with an axe, throw acid in my face. They feared, but I didn't. I wasn't going to hide from myself anymore. What you asked for was forgiveness. That's something we should all be given. After our final goodbye, I went inside my car and broke down. At first, my intentions were to see you suffer, the way I did for the ten years we were together. It would give me great pleasure, but it was wrong of me to feel this way. I shouldn't. You don't deserve it. Nobody does. I'd be the worst kind of human being if I thought this way. I realized that while writing my book, the real Puto was me.

Truth is that even though you might have lost me, you found your true self — that's more important. In the final countdown to our breakup 5...4...3...2...1... we exploded. The aftermath—the pain was needed for me to begin the process of loving myself, and you should, too.

Jason, I hope that after reading our flaws, you don't take your life, rather you save it.

CHAPTER THIRTY-FIVE

FIN

I never had a chance to say goodbye because I was angry and hurt; together that is not a good combination. The way my Uncle Chunky let his family control who he could see and couldn't see. His siblings and I weren't able to attend his funeral. Throwing Los Alacranes under the bus after the release of my first book because they supported me. Protesting against my book when all I wanted to do was share Nando with the world because it was my promise to him when he was alive. So I must come to terms and say, I love you, Chunk. I avoided crying. I didn't cry when I heard the news of your death because I didn't have any feelings towards you at the time. I had to come to peace with our situation before I could say a true goodbye, so here it goes:

In the small town of Blythe, where kids share their strawberries with flies, where the only jobs are slaved in the fields or in the prisons, where the sun with her strong rays and no mercy settle into the backs of the farmers, where the Palo Verde trees dry from heat, where the yellow jackets are ready to sting your ass, where chickens and pigs roam in front yards, where snakes curl inside dirt holes, where cactuses grow as tall as houses, where the river parties are thrown, Ramon Moroyoqui Sánchez was born.

His mother was a Yaqui from Sonora, Mexico the land where medicine women cure the sick and melt the sand with one touch. Fita stopped Ramon in his tracks as he ran through the kitchen. "Sit down," Fita ordered, placing a hand-me-down guitar on his lap, the guitar smelling of oil wood and tobacco, the way a guitar should smell. His virgin fingers round and thick, "Place your finger here," Fita directed in Spanish, her only known language. Ramon resisted at first longing to play in the streets squirming uncomfortably in his seat. On Saturdays, the white and green truck slowly drove down the streets spraying for mosquitos. Ramon hid behind trashcans patiently waiting for the truck to pass him, and once it did, he ran behind the exhaust pipe, drowning himself in the smoke along with the rest of the neighborhood kids.

"I'll miss the truck."

"*No mi importa*," Fita didn't care, "*pon tu dedo aqui*," she firmly directed pressing his fingers against the nylon string. Huffing and puffing, Ramon eventually listened, attempting his first strum, "Like this?" The strings echoed off tune. "*Si. Hace lo otra vez.*" Ramon repeated his strumming. Fita sang the lyrics of *Me Voy Pa'l Pueblo*. "*Me voy pa'l pueblo. Hoy es mi dia. Voy a alegrar toda el alma mia. I'm leaving for the town. Today is my day. I will cheer up my whole soul.*" Fita's voice, like silk, moved the earth and the sky together. She wore an apron stained with *maza*, her black hair tied in a bun, her skin the color of honey, and her tired feet in flat *huaraches*. "You and Prieto will learn to play that song. You can't go outside until you get the cord right," and Fita kept her word until she was satisfied. The flame from the *comal* rose, but that didn't break Fita's concentration. Even with Mon dehydrated in the fields and Buya chasing Lin in the living room, Fita's main priority was passing down the gift of music.

The first Alacran gig was held at Palo Verde High School, the only high school in town. The two *carnales* wore bandanas folded just above their eyebrows with Yaqui hair down to their shoulders. Lin, in the way like always, was ordered by his brothers to hold the mic and stand still, which took some effort on Lin's part. Ramon and Prieto sang to the student body preparing for the next rally. Then, it was off to work with Mon.

Ramon worked in the fields during the summer, overheard Mon's boss, "Your boy will make me a fine farmer, ya' hear. Have that boy ready. I have big plans for him," El Jefe spit with a toothpick dangling in his mouth. He was a stubby man, bald, with a pop belly and suspenders holding up his pants. Ramon stared at Mon, who purposely ignored his son's pleading eyes, "Yes, sir. *Si Señor*. My boy will be your next farmer."

"*No le ponle caso*," Fita said to Ramon when he returned home, "don't pay attention to your dad's boss. Play that guitar. Play it until it becomes a part of your body." With a revolution in mind, Ramon and Prieto packed their guitars, abandoning the land of no promises. El Jefe's expression was in complete shock when Ramon didn't return to work. The rusty truck, with tires kicking the dusty road back into its roots, and all of Blythe was bundle into one suitcase. Fita packed a brown bag full of meat and bean burritos. "If you leave, you must respect your place on earth," she held the truck door opened before Ramon could close it, "Buya is waiting for you in San Diego and take Lin with you." Lin jumped in the back of the truck, knocking on the back window and sticking out his tongue at his brothers, who weren't thrilled about the idea of a road trip with him. Ramon whistled before taking off, the whistled sounded like a freight train ready for blast off. "Ayyyeee! Hiiiyyy Hiiiyyy!" Ramon howled when he drove off, "Com'on. Let's leave this jive sucker." The truck in full gear swaying back and forth on the cracked road whipping pass the only liquor store, the only gas station, the dry bushes and trees, pass men in straw hats, with the distance turning orange, Ramon drove forward without looking back.

I was bouncing on the canvas trampoline with Nando, our bodies flipping in the air as we laughed and fell into each other's arms at the red house, where Fita and Mon migrated when they decided to finally leave Blythe, too. My hair tangled in knots and my jeans ripped with a whole on each knee. Nando wore his share of torn clothes as well, but we were merry children bathing in the sun. Nana with her same stained apron cooked in the kitchen, and Tata smoked his *puro*. My dad doing the splits, falling like a cartoon; Aunt Virgie cussing at him; Tio Rick and Uncle Chunky playing with Los Lobos, Cesar wearing his cool dark shades once again. An ice chest full of Miller Lite, flies camping out at the rim of a beer can. The backyard parties Chicano style.

So on the day you left us, there was now a greater sense of responsibility for me to share your stories I locked away in my journal. Selfish of me to keep them to myself, but now they're released into our earth, a time where the people need it the most. You have accomplished what most only dream. What a great admiral appreciation we owe you and Rick for the music, the culture, and the history. With the stories you shared, I found myself.

Tio Rick arranged for Father Ned to read you your last rights, same priest who read Fita and Mon's rights. You shut your eyes with such ease, your breath still. The room prayed for its warrior as women soothed the weeping men. We gathered at Chiquita's for your final celebration. Tio Rick strummed his guitar, a light flashed through the window and sparkled on his guitar. The *primos* drove in from Blythe, gathered in from parts of *Aztlán* to wish you farewell. Rudy Gonzales, son of activist Corky Gonzales, traveled with the Crusaders from Denver. One time, Rudy was crossing the border and was asked how long he stayed in Mexico, he replied, "Five thousand years, mother fuckers." Tio Rick saluted to a picture of you holding Nando when he was a baby with the same smile and same gap that makes me love him even more. Tio Rick sang the words, *Me Voy Pa'l Pueblo*. The place jammed packed with love, and we salute you because it was your time. We raised our glasses in the air like rifles, like a revolution.

"Hasta siempre, Comandante Chunky!

"Hasta siempre, Los Alacranes!"

Writing *Puto* took me on an incredible journey, the one unexpected, repairing broken relationships with Jason, my parents, with you, and most importantly, myself. To everyone, you were their hero, their larger than life icon, but I had the honor of calling you *familia*. Sitting in my backyard I began writing about you, and the wind blew hard, my hair covered my face, a freezing chill gushed over me, and pages from my journal flipped so rapidly I couldn't catch them. My poster board, organized with chapters, trembled and collapsed faced down. Something caught my eye from the side; it was a hummingbird within arm's reach. He stared at me zipping his speedy wings, floating in the air in place, like a painting. When I gazed at him, he looked back, but he wasn't scared. He stayed with me as I continued to write. A tear emerged, and I smiled at him. He nodded and returned back into the peaceful rays of the sun, to the place he called home—to where he finally belonged.

EPILOGUE

NAH, NOT QUITE FINISH YET

At the time that I was writing *Puto*, several unfortunate events occurred globally: the racism in Charlottesville; hurricanes in Florida, Texas, Puerto Rico, and Cuba; earthquakes in Mexico and Japan; fires in my hometown of San Diego; daily murders of innocent black and brown people; the deportation of immigrants; the ban of Muslims—it's all too much. It is difficult to find peace and love in a world of chaos. How could one come to terms or make sense of what's going on in the world when we hate too fast and love too slow. We are left with nothing but unanswered questions, closing our eyes and turning our heads in disparity, pretending the problems vanish. If one things is promised to all of us, it is death. Every day stories die, untold, trapped inside one's mind. It's too late for those who didn't feel worthy of sharing themselves, their vulnerability. When we allow ourselves to be vulnerable, that's when we become our strongest, and we can finally create.

When I began to write *Puto*, the beginning was written in rage, but as you can see, it was more than that. The book changed because I changed. I come to realize the book is not about me, but about the world and me trying to make sense of it to help my reader. What we can bring daily, what we can transcribe in our lives, what we can create. The arts can be used for good or ill intentions. We live in our comfort zones believing tomorrow is promised, like life is guaranteed. It is only when we face death that we decided to truly live, but by then, it's too late.

However, if you're reading this, it's not too late for you to share your story.

Through my writing, I pray we can unite for the betterment of humanity. We can choose to stay in sorrow, ignore, blame others, judge each other, or we can choose our creativity.

Uncertainty creates fear, fear creates comfort zones, and we become tangled in the world's problems that we forget about our potential. So often we become robots to society's norms and expectations that we forget about unleashing the creative genius inside us. I hope, as you flipped through the pages, you were closed off to the daily commotion around the world, and you remembered, even for a brief moment, who you really are, but more importantly, remember the artist who waits inside you.

ACKNOWLEDGMENTS

I cannot take the credit of writing this book when there were so many people pushing me behind the scenes and holding me accountable to get it done.

First, my praise to God who gives me the guidance and strength to write. Without him, I'm nothing.

To my parents who put up with me—thank you for giving me the gift of life. I'm grateful God chose you two as my parents. I love you.

To my family— I'm lucky to come from two strong families, Sánchez and Pedroza, who always show their support. I love you all.

To Rosi for hooking up the beautiful foreword—I am forever in depth to you for your loyalty all these years. I love you, amiga.

To Iris who plays many roles— mentor, advisor, business partner, agent, but more importantly, the role of a true, genuine friend. I love you, amiga.

To the strong women behind me—Virg, Glory, Lily, Adie, Sunny, Liz, Marianne, Tex, Aunt Bea, Sandra, Norma, Charissa, Miss Elaine, Lorraine, and Nasty— thank you for setting a strong example.

To the strong men behind me—Tio Rick, Tio Peter, Bill, Carlos, Manny, Caesar, Paul, Gio, Miklo, Dice Pilot, Pimp Nugget, Timmer, Mad Money, Pointman, Misfit, Pit Boss, Tommy, Ronnie and GTC— your love and support means everything to me.

To Guero—my deepest gratitude for keeping me grounded and pushing me forward to write when I was tired. Best wishes on your journey to healing. I love you and the G-man.

To Tom and his team, especially John for all the times you answered my calls, text, and emails in the middle of the night— you're the best.

To Joe and Sydney— you guided me to find my voice as a writer when I was sitting in your class, and I'm forever grateful for you both. You're an inspiration to me and all of your students.

To Jenna and Tina—I miss my Pilates beauties, but you are always in my heart.

To Beto— words cannot describe your talent. Your talent has no limits. Thank you for being the beautiful artist you were meant to be and sharing your gifts with the world. More projects for us lie ahead.

To Rafa— thank you for sharing and trusting me with your incredible story. A new friendship has bonded between us, and I admire your unbelievable fight through life.

To my baby boy Mr. Zach Attack— mommy loves you with all her heart. You're the best dog in the world.

To my reader— my deepest gratitude to you for all your unconditional support and love. I love you.

Made in the USA
Las Vegas, NV
09 August 2023

75884227R00094